Island
of Cyclones

by

WYNNE MAY

Harlequin Books

TORONTO·LONDON·NEW YORK·AMSTERDAM
SYDNEY·HAMBURG·PARIS·STOCKHOLM

Original hardcover edition published in 1979
by Mills & Boon Limited

ISBN 0-373-02321-9

Harlequin edition published March 1980

For Julian

———————————————————————

Printed in U.S.A.

CHAPTER ONE

THE take-off had surprised her because, except for the thrusting and tilting sensation, there had been little else to indicate that the giant airliner was airborne. With a small sigh of relief she had opened her blue eyes. She had made it, and without hysterics. She was flying again. The only difference was that she was in a jet airliner, and it was amazing how motionless it was. She had ordered a whisky and ginger-ale and she had ordered it on purpose, to steady her shaking and fainting nerves. That had been soon after take-off, and she now found herself relaxing temporarily and almost enjoying the flight from Australia to Mauritius.

Beside her the handsome dark stranger was saying, 'Would you care to exchange seats with me?' He spoke English with a French accent, or so Jade thought, and seeing that he was on his way to Mauritius this could be so.

'No, thank you,' she replied, and fear came back and showed in her dark blue eyes. 'I'm quite happy here. I don't particularly want to look down.' She gave him a small uncertain smile. If only he knew! she found herself thinking.

'It was obvious to me,' he went on, his strange dark green eyes going over her face, 'that you were very nervous. Now, however, you appear to have relaxed and I thought, to complete this, you might like the window seat.'

'No, *really*? I'm surprised you noticed. Was it *that*

obvious?' She even managed a low laugh and then bit her lip.

'Yes.' His eyes held hers. 'It was very obvious.' Tanned and handsome, he appeared used to flying ... unconcerned and completely at ease.

'Well,' she shrugged her shoulders, 'it's marvellous what a valium before take-off and a whisky, soon after, can do.' She glanced away. At thirty-eight thousand feet the drinks trolley was on its way again, before lunch.

'Valium—that is a tranquilliser, no?' he said.

Suddenly on the defensive, Jade turned to look at him. 'Yes. My doctor prescribed them for me.' What right had he to query this?

'He prescribed the valium, but *not* the whisky to go along with it. You don't mix the two.'

'I allowed a certain period of time to elapse.' Her voice was on the stiff side now. She turned to look at him again and their eyes met. His skin was naturally dark and, into the bargain, he was excitingly sun-tanned and the tan somehow accentuated those dark, sea-green eyes. The colour of his eyes came almost as a jolt, for one would have expected them to be brown—or even blue. He was the kind of man most women would give anything for as a lover and there was an indefinable magnetism about him. Shivering slightly, Jade was acutely aware of him. He would, she thought, assert himself in every role he played, including that of lover.

'I also happen to suffer from claustrophobia,' she told him. 'I don't enjoy being cooped up in a pressurised cabin.'

'Well,' he hoisted rather than shrugged those elegant shoulders, 'claustrophobia, in many cases, relates to a person who has a power psychology and cannot stand being frustrated and closed in—but it's not so bad up here in this pressurised cabin, surely?'

'I prefer not to think too much about it,' she said, 'if you don't mind.' She felt herself beginning to panic again. The sensation of being suspended in space was terrifying.

He must have sensed this because he said, 'Look about you ... at the comfortable seats, the built-in fitments. It is all so ordinary.'

'Yes.' Her voice was small and tight. 'It is.' For a moment she concentrated on these things and the image of herself being projected in cloud, high above the earth, faded and banished the feeling of vertigo and claustrophobia.

Her face was pert and her eyes a startling dark blue framed by shoulder-length dark hair with almost tawny streaks in it. Like the man next to her, she was beautifully tanned from the Australian sun, where she had spent a year, after leaving England with her brother who had gone to farm there.

'You are going to holiday in Mauritius?' he asked.

'I'm going to settle there,' she told him, turning slightly so that she could look at him. Was that an airpocket? Fright leapt back into her eyes. But no, everything seemed to be in order and, radiating confidence, a stewardess smiled and passed on up the aisle. Height and speed were meaningless once more.

'Mauritius is an earthly paradise,' he went on, 'and earthly paradises are becoming rare. On the world map, our tiny country is just a speck, but it is a paradise of white and golden beaches, palms and casuarina trees. Our mountains are quite fantastically shaped, created by volcanic eruptions. But perhaps you have already been there?'

'No, I haven't. This will be my first time. So Mauritius is your home?' Jade tried to keep the interest she was feeling from showing in the tone of her voice.

'Yes, it is. I was born in France, but I have made Mauritius my country because, moving as I do in a seemingly fast world of computers, I need a serene atmosphere. I am a very-involved-with-life person. I travel a lot. I have to, as a matter of fact. My work brings this about.'

The plane droned on and on. Passengers went through a routine of dozing, eating, drinking. The jets gulped up the kilometres and somehow, with the exciting presence of the man next to her, Jade managed to cope with her fear of flying.

A stewardess was handing out forms which had to be filled in by the passengers and, high above a glinting ocean, Jade gave her attention to this task while a feeling of panic began to mount within her. What goes up must come down, she found herself thinking a little wildly.

Some time later she heard her neighbour say, 'Let me check your seat-belt for you,' and she experienced a physical weakening as the announcement came over. 'In a few moments we shall be landing in Mauritius. Kindly fasten your seat-belts and extinguish all cigarettes.'

Flinching from the words, Jade knew she was going to pieces again and was too frightened to feel embarrassed about it. Watching the man's hands at work, she said, 'Thank you. Don't take any notice of me. Fear of a crowded room, or an elevator, I can handle, because I can always leave when I want. It's not like being trapped in a hideous jet airliner.'

'Stop thinking along these lines!' He sounded frankly irritated by her remark.

The seats tilted and they began the descent and, almost immediately, the giant airliner appeared unstable. With reverse-thrusting engines roaring it jerked and shuddered and the noise was terrifying. 'I can't stand these touch-downs and take-offs,' muttered Jade, closing her eyes. When she dared to open them again she caught glimpses of vast sugar cane plantations. 'Oh no!' she exclaimed. 'Oh, no! I can't bear this, honestly.'

'It's all right, I tell you.' He had authority, obviously, and was demonstrating it now. 'Pull yourself together.'

'Just leave me,' she told him. 'Oh, just leave me.' With surging terror she lifted an arm and began reaching for the dial which would give her air. 'Air ... I just want air. Would you? Please? Oh, do something!'

'One moment.' She felt him fidgeting beside her. 'Is that better?' he asked.

Shaking her head, she said, 'No. No. I feel awful—I can't help it. I'm terrified and I feel awful. Right now, nothing can help. I'm sorry I'm being such a nuisance—such a coward.'

There were two loud thumps and the plane made sickening lurches.

He took her hand and she clung to it. 'It is nothing,' he told her. 'Just relax, you silly little thing.'

'Will it never end?' she whispered, and bit her lip.

She was aware of the rising roar of the powerful engines and felt the aircraft's protesting brakes and then the entire plane seemed to be falling apart. The passengers were very still and the tension was unbearable. Opening her eyes, Jade noticed two stewardesses strapped into previously vacant seats and the girls appeared, to her, tense and apprehensive. Then someone was whistling *The Way We Were* and Jade knew that, if she lived to be a hundred, she would never forget that tune.

Touching down on time, the Boeing began to dip towards the runway and the roar of its turbo-jet engines reached a crescendo as it began to taxi at alarming and, so it seemed, increasing speed.

'Captain Murray hopes you have enjoyed your flight.' The voice was electronically polite and, suddenly, everything was orderly again.

'Are we down?' Jade asked stupidly, still clinging to the dark stranger's well-shaped hand.

'Yes.' She imagined she could hear the smile in his voice. 'Look,' he went on, still holding her hand while she became acutely aware of this, 'quite apart from the fact that you appear to have a very earnest fear of flying, let me say that I have done this many, many times and it has never been as rough as this.'

'So it *was* rough?' Relief showed in her eyes.

'Yes. It is possibly very windy outside.' His eyes held hers and suddenly her fingers seemed to be throbbing within the confines of his own.

'It's nice of you to say so,' she smiled. 'I—I'm just a coward, let's face it. How did it feel to be sitting next to a coward?' Her blue eyes were faintly mocking now. 'I'm terribly sorry for being such a nuisance to you.' His fingers on her own were a seduction of her senses and her eyes became serious.

'I thrive on variety, when it come to the opposite sex,' he said, releasing her fingers. 'This is the first time that I have sat next to *such* a coward—and certainly the most beautiful. I can honestly claim to have sat next to the most beautiful coward.' He laughed softly and those sea-green eyes went briefly over her.

'W-well, you're honest, anyway—about the coward, I mean,' she stammered.

They were the last to leave the plane.

'We touched down on time,' he said conversationally, as they stepped on to the tarmac. The wind caught at Jade's hair and swirled it about her face and she shook it back.

'Yes.' She discovered that her legs were still shaking.

'Let us not be so solemn,' he mocked her. 'It is all over now.'

'Yes, I know, but I'm still shaking—like a fool.' She turned to look at him.

Situated about three miles from the coast, on the south-east, and amidst the green sugar cane, Plaisance Airport welcomed them with its pink hibiscus and palms, swaying in the wind. Glancing about her, Jade came to the conclusion that the flavour of the island was a mixture of races, customs, creeds, cultures and languages.

'Thank you for taking an interest in me,' she said, clutching at her windswept hair. 'It did help, believe me.'

'Then I was of some help?' He looked at her with an expression that unnerved her.

'Yes, very much so. It's—a long story—about this terror I have, of flying. It's just—something that—happened.' Her voice dragged.

Regarding her with interest, he did not pursue the matter but said instead, 'I see. Well, I hope you get over this terror—in time.'

Her blue eyes were suddenly troubled and unhappy. 'I hope so too.'

However, life was suddenly beautiful and very simple now that they had landed safely.

'You are being met?' he was asking.

'Yes. By American Express.'

'I see.' After a moment he said, 'But no, this I don't see. You are to settle here—and yet there is nobody to welcome you, except for American Express?'

'I've come here to be married,' she told him, and for some unknown reason it was not easy to speak casually. 'He's away at present, but the Comtesse de Spéville has arranged for American Express to meet me. As a matter of fact, I'm going to work for her. You might have heard of her health and beauty clinic—the Coral Reef?' She stood to one side now, to allow two other people to pass her.

'In other words, Nicole de Spéville is expecting you?'

'So you know Nicole?' There was interest in Jade's voice.

'Yes.' Their eyes met and held. Suddenly he said, 'I dislike crowds—they affront me. Let's get through the formalities.'

Although formalities at the passport and health control took time, there were no hassles. It seemed inevitable that they should scan the conveyor belts for their luggage together. Jade collected hers and then parted with it again, after Customs officials had made chalk marks on the cases. Her eyes were now free again to search for the man whose name she did not even know, but somehow he had vanished into the crowd and she felt alone and completely apart from the crowd.

'Miss Lawford?'

Turning, Jade said, 'Yes?'

'Welcome to Mauritius. I am from American Express. Both Marlow Lewis and the Comtesse de Spéville arranged that I should meet you at the same time as I meet up with my tourists. You are to travel with us in the mini-bus. Did you have a pleasant flight?'

'Yes, thank you.' Looking at the girl, who was wearing white slacks and a black and white shirt, Jade wondered why she felt let down. After all, this was only what she had expected. Her face remained neutral, however, while her eyes slid past the girl from American Express, searching for the dark stranger with the strange sea-green eyes. A black Mauritian was taking care of her luggage now and there was nothing for it but to follow the girl in the white slacks. She took a calming breath. Well, that was that ... unless, of course, she met him again, through Nicole de Spéville. The realisation that she might caused her heart to miss a beat.

They went out into the sun and the wind which was very strong and which had, no doubt, been responsible for a 'rough' landing, as the man had referred to it.

The flight had, in fact, been better than she had expected and she had even experienced a kind of peace, while flying, which was surprising, really ... a kind of freedom, an almost mystic relationship between the ocean far below, and space.

People milled about them. Small, dark-skinned girls pestered Jade to buy shells and necklaces and golden bananas.

'I am Vivienne, ma-dom. Please buy.'

'I am Domaingue, ma-dom. You buy from *me*. Please!'

Apparently they were used to the young lady from American Express, as they did not worry her to buy.

'I have none of your money right now,' stammered Jade, becoming embarrassed and confused.

'I take Australian money, ma-dom. No worry.'

'I'm very sorry, really. I have no money at the moment—only traveller's cheques,' answered Jade, eager to keep up with the girl from American Express.

'But you came on Australian plane, ma-dom. *Please!*' The young voice was accusing.

Feeling mean, Jade pushed her way through the thick crowd of people.

At the mini-bus she watched her luggage being wheeled in her direction and, satisfied that it was on its way, she glanced around, excited. Even from this point, amidst the traffic and confusion which goes along with an airport, she could see the sugar cane for which the island was known and those mountains, which seemed to have been heaved into shape by gigantic volcanic eruptions many ages ago and which had, in fact, been created in this manner.

Next to Jade a handsome and tanned priest was waiting his turn to have his luggage stacked into the small bus.

'Hello, Father. You remember me. I am Domaingue, Father. You always buy from me when you return to Mauritius.'

'Not now,' he told her. 'I always buy from you when I go back from my holiday. You know that, Domaingue.'

'But, Father. . . .'

'You're a persistent small girl, Domaingue. I'll buy from you when I return home in two weeks' time.'

Jade remained standing where she was, the wind having its way with her hair and her dusky-pink Italian cashmere suit which was just a shade darker than the oleander bushes forming a low hedge to one side of where the minibus was parked.

Here, on this island, she was sure was everything she

was going to need to be luxuriously content ... golden sunshine, coral reefs—and where every look, every smile was like a melodious note, bringing about that symphony which could only be Mauritius and where France, Africa and India met in a tropical island paradise of creamy beaches, lush gorges and those dramatic mountain peaks.

When she turned she caught her breath when she saw her flight companion who was exchanging greetings with the girl from American Express, and when his eyes met hers, she was aware of a feeling of exhilaration. Coming towards her, he said, 'When I turned round back there, you were gone. Where did you get to?'

'The same place as you did,' she replied lightly. 'I was completely swallowed up.'

'Well, now that I have found you again I will drive you to the Hotel Chalain. My car has been delivered to the airport and is waiting.'

'But ...' she lifted her shoulders and laughed a little, 'how do you know I'm going to the Hotel Chalain?'

'Obviously you are going there, if you were about to board this mini-bus. Besides, that is where Nicole de Spéville has her health clinic, no? Or are you going to her house, which is quite close to the hotel?'

'I'm going to the hotel, but....'

'No buts,' he told her. 'I will arrange for your luggage to be taken to my car. I have already spoken to the young lady, as a matter of fact.'

'You have?' Jade widened her eyes. 'Well!' She tried to sound annoyed. He was, she was thinking, a man who was capable of sincerity and who would be tender and gentle, on the one hand—but tough and hard, on the other. Although she felt she could trust him, it was just that things were moving too fast for her. 'I am expected to arrive on the mini-bus,' she went on, and then noticed that the girl from American Express had disappeared into the building which they had just recently left. The Indian driver, who looked cool in a white safari suit, was supervising the luggage.

'Allow me to remind you that I am a friend of Nicole de Spéville,' he said, and put out a hand to stop Jade's luggage from going into the vehicle.

'And you think that makes everything all right?' Jade's smile was mocking. 'I don't even know your name and I am, after all, in a strange country.'

'I was coming to that,' he said easily. 'My name is Laurent Sevigny.' She liked the cutting precision of his voice and the air of male authority about him. Her blue eyes flickered over him and she knew that he would be a man who would have an instinctive feeling for human weaknesses in other people.

After a moment, because she knew it was expected of her, she said, 'I'm Jade Lawford.'

'I see.' He gave her a leisurely look. 'Since the days of the velvet hatbox and the use of surnames, even here in Mauritius, I believe, are gone, I will begin by calling you Jade. And now....' There was confusion about her luggage. 'Leave it here.' He sounded frankly irritable. 'Miss Lawford's luggage is going in my car.'

For a moment Jade went on looking at him, wide-eyed and considering, and then lifting one slim shoulder she allowed him to steer her and the porter who had come to light in the direction of his car which had been left at the airport for him to collect on his arrival.

After their luggage was stacked into his car, Laurent Sevigny, who believed that the days of the velvet hatbox and the use of surnames were gone, nevertheless opened the door, in the good old-fashioned tradition, for her. As she slipped into the seat and drew her long, elegant legs in after her, she gave him a mocking glance, but her thoughts in this connection were obviously lost on him.

As he got in beside her she turned to look at him. 'And yet ... *Laurent* ... you appear very much the velvet hatbox type.' She laughed softly.

'So?' He inserted the key and then glanced up, and because she felt the urge to draw a sharp little breath at the exciting nearness of him, she bit her lip. 'Why is that?' His strange eyes held hers.

'Well,' she shrugged, 'it's a long time since a man last deemed it necessary to open a car door for me. That, I think, puts *you* in the velvet hatbox type category. You're also very clever.' Opening her bag, she took out her sunglasses and then, behind their tinted lenses, felt less exposed to his scrutiny. She did not want him to see that she was excited by his strong dark looks and the magnetism of his sea-green eyes.

'In what way?' he asked, before starting the car.

'You've succeeded in manoeuvring me into accepting a lift from a stranger in a strange country, and I'm not sure I like that.'

After a moment he said, 'About your remark concerning the car door. I do not suffer bad manners gladly and for this reason I prefer to open doors—and to close them. It is as simple as that. That is, I think, a clumsy word, no? *Manoeuvre?* It means, if my memory serves me correctly, a deceptive movement ... a skilful planning, on my part. I have given you my credentials. I am a friend of Nicole de Spéville. There is nothing deceptive about that.' He started the car and reversed out of the parking lot and soon they were passing through a succession of settlements, which seemed to teem with life of all descriptions—dark-skinned people in colourful attire, goats, fowls, skinny dogs and even pigs and piglets. By a coincidence, the mini-bus followed. The Indian who was driving it was using his hooter constantly and it surprised Jade when Laurent Sevigny began to do the same thing, scattering people and animals to one side of the road. Suddenly she laughed, shaking her head in wonderment.

'You make James Bond look tame,' she commented.

Turning to look at her, he sounded puzzled when he queried, 'James Bond?'

'Yes—you know, Ian Fleming's character. You must have seen the films, surely?'

'Of course.' She watched him lift one tanned hand from the wheel. 'James Bond. Playing that character placed the star in question among the biggest money-earning stars in cinema history, I should imagine. Now, to what do you refer? My driving? Or the fact that I am in the company of a dazzlingly, beautifully thrown-together girl?' He turned to look at her again and his eyes went over her briefly before he gave his attention to the road.

Overall was magnificent scenery. Cane-fields, islets and glittering water. Suddenly Jade caught her breath as the mini-bus overtook them and narrowly missed a head-on collision with a huge truck which had loomed up from apparently nowhere.

Covering her mouth with her fingers, she exclaimed, 'Whew!'

'It's all a case of making decisions,' he told her easily, as if nothing had happened. 'Either I blow my horn or I run people down. Here in Mauritius it is expected of a driver to constantly sound it. In fact, a driver is despised, almost, if he does not perform this ritual on the road. If I had to slacken speed every time a person or an animal got in my way we would make little headway in Mauritius.'

'I can see that,' she admitted.

Pink hibiscus and scarlet poinsettia hedged the roads, clashing beautifully with the unique mountains, in the distance, which were mostly of dark lava rock, rising up in strange shapes.

'You have an unusual name,' he said, his voice at his most formal.

'Yes—don't ask me why. It must have been because my parents met in Singapore. My mother was very romantic.' She smiled and shrugged her shoulders.

'When I say your name in my mind I visualise a white jade phoenix bird.' She liked the way he turned to look at her, those strange dark sea-green eyes on her lips before they went to the hollow in her throat.

'Do I remind you of a phoenix bird?' she asked, laughing a little.

'Yes. I own a white jade phoenix and it is extremely beautiful.'

'I see.' She stopped laughing and bit her lip, then she said, 'Do you know, Jade also means a worn-out horse.' Embarrassed by his remark, she was trying not to show it. 'I should have thought, however, that you would have owned a jade dodo. Isn't the largest sports club in Mauritius named after the famous and extinct dodo?'

'You have been doing your homework on your new country, I see. That is good.'

'Marlow wrote about it,' she said, feeling that it was now time to introduce Marlow into the picture of things. 'He's a member.'

'Marlow? He is the man you are going to marry?' They were crossing over a bridge where down below, on the banks of the river, women were at work, thumping the dirt from bright cotton clothing on the rocks. Laurent Sevigny's voice, she thought, had changed.

'Marlow Lewis? Do you know him?' Her eyes left the women below on the rocks and went to the bracelet she was wearing and she began moving it round and round on her wrist. As yet, the finger on her left hand was ringless. Soon, however, there would be an engagement ring and a plain or engraved gold band. For some unknown reason a shudder passed over her.

'Marlow Lewis is a hunter,' his voice was curt now. 'I know him slightly. We do not move in the same circles.' He sounded rude now.

'He's a sugar farmer,' Jade said softly.

'He is also a hunter.'

After a confused moment she said, 'I didn't know that. In fact, I didn't know there were wild animals on this island.'

'No? Well, the shooting season lasts three months. It is the winter sport of the island's privileged set. It is known to the French-speaking community as *la chasse*. Three thousand head or so of game are shot down every year, to the great delight of the hunter. It was the Dutch who introduced deer from Java.'

'I. . . .' Suddenly Jade felt sick. 'I didn't know. Marlow didn't mention this in his letters to me. Do you hunt?' She turned to look at Laurent Sevigny, impatient for his reply.

'Like the deer,' he said, 'this paradise is also my home. I am not a hunter.'

'I see.' She let out a breath. 'Where do you live—on the island?'

'I own a house within easy distance of the hotel.'

'You,' she fidgeted with her bracelet again, 'must be married, in that case?'

Turning to look at her, he snapped. 'Why? Just because I happen to live in a house? But no, I am a confirmed bachelor.' Suddenly he looked amused and his eyes mocked her.

Why did she feel so crazily happy? she asked herself. What difference did it make? She was here to marry Marlow Lewis. She supposed she loved Marlow. After all, corresponding for two years had drawn them very close.

To steady herself she said, 'Tell me, what are all those pyramid-like things in the sugar fields? I can't help noticing them. Mound after mound of them.'

'They are piles of volcanic rock,' he told her. 'They have been dug up from the earth and piled up that way.'

'And that sweet and heady scent?' she asked.

'It is the scent of the sugar-cane. As you have probably noticed by now, sugar cane grows everywhere in Mauritius, even right down to the sea and fringing the towns. We have just passed a mill, back there. The smell was heavy there.'

'For a small island,' she observed, 'we seem to have travelled a long distance from the airport.'

'We are nearly there,' he told her. 'Soon you will meet Nicole de Spéville—if not Marlow Lewis.'

Jade remained silent and then he said, 'We were talking about jade. Apart from the house, I own a chalet which is in the beautiful grounds of the hotel and this chalet is set like a piece of pale jade on the green lawn.'

'You sound like a very fortunate person,' she an-

swered, 'to own both a house and a chalet.' While she
was speaking, she found herself wondering what Marlow's plantation house was like. She would go there
after she was married. Marlow had written to say that
it was close enough to the health clinic for her to travel
there in the little Mini he was going to provide for her.

'I think about it all the time,' Laurent told her,
'make no mistake. I know I am fortunate.'

A gauzy heat seemed to hang over the island. It all
seemed so unreal, she thought, aware of the handsome
man beside her and frightened about what it was that
was happening to her. She couldn't stop what was happening to her, and she fussed with her bracelet and
caught her breath when his fingers caught her own.

'Why are you so nervous?' he asked. He lifted her
hand and put it on the seat, beside his thigh, still holding it, and she could feel the warmth of it and the
warmth of those strong, tanned fingers. He transferred
his fingers to her wrist and kept her hand there, close
to him. 'When you arrive,' he went on, 'you will enjoy
an island cocktail, I think.' He turned to look at her.
'Are you feeling the heat?'

'No—not after Australia,' she answered, trying to
keep her voice light and easy but finding this difficult.

'Marlow Lewis is an Australian, I know,' he said.
'You, however, do not strike me as being Australian.
Why is this, do you think? Is it because of your very
British accent?'

'I am British,' she told him. 'I was only a year in
Australia. I went there with my brother Jeffrey. He and
Marlow....' She broke off, remembering. 'A-and *you*?
Were you on holiday in Australia?'

'No. I merely went there to purchase one or two rare
pieces of porcelain from a private collection there.'

She was curious. 'Do you collect porcelain, then?'

He seemed to be thinking for a moment. 'It is a long story. You see, my family in France were all collectors. When I was, let me see, about eighteen years, my mother purchased a pair of flambé Sung Dynasty vases and I was intrigued. I was attracted to Chinese porcelain. My own first pieces were very expensive, I can tell you.' He laughed suddenly. 'Perhaps this is why they became the foundation for my collection. I search for values, not bargains. To my mind, a bargain-hunter loses out. That is how I started. From being a collector, I went into business. In France, of course, and then I came out here and started a business here in Curepipe.'

Suddenly he laughed. 'Don't for a moment, please, think that my life revolved around famille rose and gold *médaillon*. I was interested in sport, study, friends ... *girls*.' He lifted her hand and placed her wrist against his lips, gave her a challenging look and then he became serious. 'You were talking about your brother Jeffrey—and Marlow.'

'Yes.' Jade lifted her shoulders. 'Well, they went into partnership together. Marlow had a sheep station there and, using an inheritance from my father, Jeffrey became part-owner. He'd met Marlow while on holiday in Australia, and then I joined Jeffrey in Australia.'

'He is still running this sheep station?' Laurent spoke against her wrist and Jade could feel his warm breath there. The tune which someone had whistled on the plane as it landed came to her mind—*The Way We Were*.

'Jeffrey is no longer alive,' she said, very softly.

Taking her wrist from his lips and placing her hand back on the soft leather seat, he said, 'I see. I am sorry.'

'Last year he lost his life in an air crash.' Her voice was suddenly flat.

'That explains everything to me, of course. Your fear of flying,' he said.

'I was in that plane,' she went on. 'So was Marlow. The plane—a light one—actually belonged to Marlow and Jeffrey crashed it. It was Jeffrey's fault. We moved into heavy cloud. Marlow was saying something to Jeffrey and he sounded angry. Before that, I'd noticed a road below, and then we saw the mountain. Jeffrey swerved the plane—upwards. There was another girl in the plane with us. She was killed. She was engaged to Marlow. After that it all remains a complete blank to me, but it was the pain I was feeling that forced me to try to pull myself together. We were all outside the plane. I was on my back, with the wing almost on top of me. There were cars on the road, far below, but of course we—Marlow and I—couldn't reach them. We were hurt. I didn't even know that Jeffrey and Elisa were dead. Everything blacked out again and the next thing I remember was people with blankets and hot coffee. We were taken to an ambulance by helicopter and then to hospital. They said how Marlow and I survived was a miracle. I spent three months on my back. I vowed I'd never fly again. I can't even bear to hear a plane above me, let alone fly in one.'

He was quiet for such a long time, giving his attention to driving, that Jade felt she shouldn't have embarrassed him by telling him. Finally he said, 'I think it must be true what they say—that love is a many-splendoured thing. It is nature's way of giving a reason to everything. Once, on a high and cloud-misted mountain, you lost the brother you loved, and a friend, but your love for Marlow Lewis taught you how to sing again ... how to fly.'

When she made no reply he turned to look at her, and her lashes went down. Very softly she said, 'Yes.'

A picture of Marlow Lewis as she remembered him came to mind ... older than she was by twenty years. That made him forty-one. There was a faintly chilling quality about him which went along with his reddish-blond hair and beard and his cool, almost tawny eyes. Marlow got on well with younger people and this was no doubt due to the fact that he appealed to a generation for which coolness is everything. He always projected a kind of recklessness. That hardness, she knew, was for real. He always enjoyed winning and when he lost he could be unpleasant.

'Marlow always enjoyed winning,' she said, without thinking.

'I can imagine,' Laurent Sevigny replied quietly. 'After the hunt is always a social occasion and more often than not rounded off with a noisy champagne luncheon at one of the shooting lodges. He always attends. I know.'

'He—er—seems to have a natural instinct for contemporary fashion,' she went on. 'Do you know, Marlow seems to have a kind of natural instinct—a knack —of making other people, of his own age, I mean, appear *old*.'

'I have worked this out,' he said, 'while we have been driving. He must be older than you by twenty years.'

'Yes, he is.'

Often in the last few months Jade had asked herself whether she really loved Marlow Lewis and, in turn, whether he had ever got over Elisa, the girl who had lost her life because of a careless approach to flying on the part of Jeffrey.

In the distance, now, she could see the curling pencil line of the coral reef, whitely scalloping what appeared to be a magnificent palm-fringed beach.

'We are nearly there,' Laurent Sevigny said. 'A custom is that you are shown to your room where you may ring through for an island cocktail of your own choice. On the other hand, however, you might well prefer to have it in the open-air lounge ... open to the sea-breezes.'

'That sounds wonderful,' she answered. 'I look forward to that. What goes into the cocktail?'

He lifted one shoulder and turned to her and she was acutely aware of the way in which his eyes met, and held, her own. 'Oh, a dash of this and a dash of that.' He smiled and then changed down as they approached a blind and dangerous bend in the road.

'It sounds intriguing,' she said. She spoke in the carefully modulated voice she always used when she felt unsure of herself.

CHAPTER TWO

A DELICIOUS breeze blew off the sea. The hotel, which was set in a colourful palm-strewn garden shared only by its own and a few private chalets, greeted her with its pink oleanders and pink hibiscus.

Laurent Sevigny parked the car in front of the foyer and turned to look at her. 'Put it like this,' his dark sea-green eyes went over her, 'I have enjoyed meeting you, being with you.'

'I must have been a nuisance to you,' Jade said, 'on the plane.' She was aware of the strong natural grace about him. It was a grace the average man did not possess—almost frightening, because of that strength she knew was there.

'On the contrary.' He glanced away. 'The mini-bus, although it overtook us at one stage, has not yet arrived. Apparently we took different routes. I will take you to Nicole.'

'Where is your chalet?' Jade asked.

'Up that way,' he told her. 'You can't see it from here.'

'It's beautiful,' she said, looking in the direction of the beach. Fishermen kept their boats under the palms and, in the distance, surf formed a ruffled white collar on the coral reef.

When she stepped out of the car she stood gazing for a moment at the hotel where she was to work. There was an air of luxury about it and a promise of what lay beyond.

Turning, she said, 'Thanks for the ride.' She smiled.

'Don't worry about your luggage,' he said, 'I will arrange for it to be taken inside.'

It was obvious that the guest-rooms, lounges, dining-room, restaurants, pool terrace, cocktail and bikini bars faced the beach and coral reef. Jade felt Laurent's warm fingers on her arm. 'This way,' he said.

They went into the air-conditioned reception foyer and a beautiful dark-skinned girl of uncertain ancestry said, 'Hello, Mr Sevigny. Welcome back. May I help you?' She glanced in Jade's direction.

'This is Miss Jade Lawford. She is to join the Comtesse de Spéville in running the hydro.'

'Oh, I see. I hope you will be happy in Mauritius,' said the girl, before answering the telephone, which had started to ring.

'I can see what you meant when you spoke of the lounge catching—or open—to the sea-breezes,' Jade said a moment later, looking at Laurent Sevigny. With its black and white floor, luxurious honey-coloured leather sofas and exotic plants the lounge, to one side of a staircase, was exciting and inviting. More pink hibiscus grew next to the pool where there was a lot of white furniture with pink cushions and sun-umbrellas to match the blooms. These colours accentuated the palms and the sea.

Bronzed by the sun, Nicole de Spéville was in her cool office, facing the coral reef. The black caftan she was wearing showed up her blonde hair which looked as if she swam a lot and did not wish to fuss over it. Her eyelashes were long and very black—and, quite obviously, false. She was so slim that her tanned skin seemed to be drawn tightly over those parts of her body which could be seen as she moved about in the long robe. Beneath the caftan her black bikini was visible.

'Laurent!' Like him, she spoke English with a strong French inflection. 'I did not know you were back. You did not even let me know. Why?'

'I decided to surprise everybody,' he said, 'and apparently I have surprised you.' Jade watched as he kissed Nicole de Spéville, surprised because of the jealousy which had sprung to life. Looking at them she was thinking that Laurent Sevigny and Comtesse Nicole de Spéville must surely qualify as the 'beautiful people' she was always reading about.

'And this is?' Nicole's eyes went over Jade. 'Not—

not a bride you have brought back, surely?' Shock showed in her blue eyes.

'I'm Jade Lawford,' Jade cut in quickly. 'You're expecting me.'

'But,' the blue eyes with their artificial lashes widened, 'I do not understand. You were supposed to be met by Judy of American Express.'

'Since we travelled together on the plane,' Laurent explained, 'I brought Jade here myself. The mini-bus has not yet arrived.'

'So? You are Jade Lawford. Marlow said that you were quite, quite beautiful, and he was right. Marlow, of course, will be gone for another whole week.' Turning to Laurent she said, 'He is fortunate, Marlow, is he not—to be marrying this child? For, like me, Marlow is in his forties.'

Jade was frankly dazzled by the Comtesse's vitality. It was difficult to believe that this beautiful woman was in her forties. She did not look that old. That old? A small shiver ran down her spine. She was going to marry a man *that old* ... in his forties, she thought confusedly. In the next moment she comforted herself by thinking that forty-this and forty-that was not so old, especially when the persons concerned looked like Nicole and Marlow ... as she remembered him.

'And so you are not yet settled in, obviously?' Nicole kept on looking at Jade, her eyes going over the dusky-pink Italian cashmere suit and bronze-coloured handbag.

'We came straight to your office,' Laurent explained.

'Well, in that case settle in,' Nicole went on. 'In about—oh, let's see, an hour ...' she shrugged her shoulders, 'an hour and a half, I'll take you along to the clinic and introduce you around.'

'Where shall I meet you?' Jade asked. 'Here?'

'Yes, make it here. Tomorrow we can begin to show you what it is we are doing here. And you, Laurent?' Nicole turned to look at him. 'What are you going to do?'

'I will see Miss Lawford to reception, arrange for her luggage to be brought in and be on my way.'

It should have all been so exciting, Jade thought, but something kept hammering at her mind. She found herself wondering whether she was going to be able to go through with marrying Marlow after all. Laurent Sevigny had made certain of that. And yet—she stole a glance at him, as they made their way back to reception—was he as attracted to her as she was to him? At that moment their eyes met and there was a marked intensity in the expression of those strange green eyes. 'Nicole is very beautiful, don't you think?' he said.

'Yes.' She was aware again of a feeling of jealousy.

They stood waiting together while her luggage was being brought into the foyer. 'Thank you,' Jade looked at Laurent uncertainly. 'I'm going to enjoy that island cocktail you were telling me about. I'll sip it while I'm unpacking.'

'After business hours,' he said, 'I like to sit and over-look the coral reef. I have a sunset drink and my mind seems free. Sometimes I listen to music. A tranquillity washes away the tensions of the day, which really are of no great importance. You will do this, with me, before Marlow Lewis gets back. Both my chalet and my house, on another part of the island, are places where I can be alone, or have twenty people. Sometimes ...' his eyes held hers, 'only two.'

At first she felt an odd little thrill, but this soon gave way to anger.

'Well, you did mention back at the airport that you dislike crowds, that a crowd affronts you, after all—so I can imagine that, and I'm sure you don't have to rely on me to form one of those intimate little twosomes.'

He seemed, she noticed, to be looking at her with a faraway kind of amusement. 'I know I don't have to rely on you for this,' he told her. 'I only know that, now that I have met you, I have got to go as far as I can go with you.' Suddenly he smiled. 'Enjoy your cocktail.'

She watched him go ... dark and handsome, with eyes an odd shade of dark-green when perhaps they should have been a very dark brown, almost black ... or tawny, at the very least, and dark hair which had been allowed to elegantly overgrow his collar. Laurent Sevigny was rich and handsome and would never be at a loss for beautiful women. She should have appreciated the logic, of course, but she couldn't. You little fool, she said to herself, what have you let this man do to you?

In her room, which had a small entrance foyer, with walk-in cupboard with louvred doors to one side of it, well-appointed bathroom and balcony, she lifted the phone and ordered a cocktail which she had chosen from a list which was on the long bamboo dressing table, and which was 'on the house'. Then she walked about the delightfully chilled room while she unpacked and thought about Laurent Sevigny when she should have been thinking about Marlow Lewis. When the cocktail arrived it was on a cane tray which had a crimson pink envelope on it across which was written: Miss Jade Lawford. When the page had gone she opened the envelope with her nail-file and shook out the card which was inside. It read: The Manager of the Hotel requests the pleasure of your company for cocktails at the bikini bar at 7.00 this evening.

Her immediate reaction to this was—would Laurent Sevigny be there? And then, reprimanding herself, she changed her thoughts to what she should wear. To be on the safe side she decided to wear a caftan. A caftan, after all, could take one most places.

When she joined Nicole in her office she noticed that the Comtesse had changed into a different caftan— white, this time, and see-through, with a black bikini showing itself tantalisingly.

'While we corresponded,' Nicole said, 'you addressed me as Comtesse de Spéville, but now that you are here, please call me Nicole.'

'Thank you,' Jade replied, 'I will.'

They went out to the terrace lounge where they could see the pool and the palms and the sea. Sun-tanned, near-nude peopde were either leaving the pool or diving into it.

Cutting across the lounge, with its black and white floor, honey-gold sofas and chairs and exotic plants in great white urns, Nicole said, 'This way, Jade. We have one whole wing to ourselves, but our clients occupy the same rooms and suites as holiday guests. They are, after all, on a beautiful holiday, although,' she chuckled, 'they cannot eat very much, poor things. They are here, after all, to get slim and fit.'

The health clinic had its own private terrace which also enjoyed the same views of palms, beach, coral reef and, to one side, the sparkling pool. The coral reef pounded with a kind of regularity. Pampered, beautiful women, with sun-streaked hair, and wearing short Nicole de Spéville towelling robes, were lounging about; all were in various stages of becoming slim, more healthy, more lovely. There were a number of tanned men about, also enjoying the treatment of the clinic.

The notice on one of the big glass doors read: Comtesse Nicole de Spéville Health and Beauty Clinic. Reception. Female Department. Sauna. Plunge Pool. Swedish Massages. Auto-Masseur. Anti-Cellulite heat. Electro-Therapy.

There was an antique desk in the reception office and an attractive Creole girl wearing a hibiscus-pink sun-frock and a sea-shell on a pendant sat in the huge wicker peacock chair behind it. Somebody was saying, 'You look very sexy today, darling.'

Nicole de Spéville looked suddenly harassed and vague, for the moment she had put in an appearance people began demanding her attention.

'We are overbooked,' she said, a moment later to Jade, and then sighed. 'But then we always *are*. Look,' she glanced in the direction of the Creole girl, 'be a darling and show Jade round, Loreto—and, Jade, join me back in my office when you are through, will you?'

The entire health and beauty clinic appeared to be curtained in shadowed hibiscus-pink, gold and apricot silk, and the floors were honey-gold tiles. There were arches everywhere and white louvred doors, urns with exotic leaves, and in the foyer there was a huge framed poster of a devastatingly beautiful naked girl on the banks of a river. A notice carried the words: Have you had your nine glasses of water today?

'Men's section to the left,' Loreto said, smiling. 'Women's section to the right. You wish to see the men's section?' She laughed impishly, for there were loud, 'naked' slaps coming from that direction. 'Armand is busy, as you can hear. In any case, in this section we have Armand, Maurice (she pronounced it Maw-reeze) and Pierre. Armand is busy with a massage now, as you can hear. So, all right, now we go through to the women's section. All staff have been trained by the Comtesse de Spéville.'

The Creole girl kept up a running commentary as she showed Jade around the clinic.

'Before you go back to her office I will show you, very quickly, the hairdressing salon and the beauty parlour,' Loreto said. 'I love the salon. It has black Indian temple furniture in it—the chairs look like black lace, with silk hibiscus-pink cushions.'

When it was over Jade found Nicole in her glass-fronted office. At the pool a Frenchman was coaching a tanned girl in the art of diving. Nicole was surrounded by files and brochures and people kept knocking on her door, or merely walking straight into the office to seek her advice on something. Here, the fine, see-through silk curtains were also in shades of hibiscus-pink, apricot and honey-gold, and the combination was at once exciting and sophisticated.

'Darling,' Nicole looked at Jade, 'go and order anything you like—a drink, maybe, a sunset snack, anything. Tomorrow we get organised, no? I am so busy now. Tell me, are you disappointed that Marlow was not here to meet you?'

After an awkward little pause Jade said, 'I expected that, of course.'

'Yes, I know—but even so.'

'Do you know Marlow well?' Jade asked.

'Yes, I do. Sometimes he gives parties at his plantation house.'

'What is it like?' Jade asked. 'Marlow's plantation house?'

'Oh,' Nicole shrugged those slim, slim shoulders, 'old

—very old. Gracious, colonial, built of tropical wood and under the constant threat of cyclones.' She laughed lightly, but Jade's nerves tightened.

'The thought of a cyclone scares me to pieces!'

'We get warnings,' Nicole said, 'and fortunately they do not occur often. I myself have experienced only one severe cyclone. Anyway, we speak later, Jade?'

'Fine.' Jade moved away from the desk.

'You will be at the cocktail party at the bikini bar?'

'Yes, Nicole.'

'And after dinner, you will have your first taste of Sega dancing,' Nicole told her.

The sky at sunset was apricot, pink and pale gold, and it matched the whole set-up, Jade thought. The palms and the filao trees swayed in a light breeze. She went upstairs and sat on her balcony for a while, then went downstairs again, and in the direction of the bikini bar.

People were already gathered there. Waiters wearing white moved through the mixed Creole, Chinese, French and European crowd, carrying trays with cocktails and snacks on them. Jade helped herself to a cocktail and sipped it slowly. She did not see anybody she recognised, even though she had met a number of people at the health and beauty clinic ... and then she saw him and their eyes met across the space which divided them. She watched him as he came towards her, drink in hand.

'You look completely refreshed,' he said, 'and very beautiful.' Those strange eyes went over her and the soft, sexy caftan, a creation in crimson silk, swirled about her ankles in the sea-breezes. They stood crushed together in the mass of people, holding their glasses. This was the time of day, Jade was quick to notice, when Laurent's eyes were beginning to change from a dark sea-green to almost malachite.

'I didn't expect to see you here.' She tried not to sound pleased and excited about this.

'Well, it is not surprising, after all. You can see my chalet from here ... see that leaning palm?' He placed an arm about her shoulders and she found herself thrilling to his touch. 'That is your landmark.' He turned to look at her face and smiled. Taking his arm away, he went on, 'I am almost part of the hotel, anyway. You see, I form part of the hotels group.'

'Oh.' This took a moment to register with her and she was confused. Was she, as a result of this, going to see more of Laurent Sevigny at the hotel? she asked herself.

'I don't recognise any of the people I was introduced to this afternoon,' she said, helping herself to a chilli-bite from a passing tray. She began to nibble at the curried savoury. 'I'm referring, of course, to the health clinic staff.'

'They do not all stay at the hotel,' he told her. 'Most of them live near to the hotel and Nicole sends a mini-bus to collect them each morning and they return home in this fashion at the end of the day. Some of them have cars of their own. The dieticians, however, remain here on the premises.'

'Oh, I see,' she murmured.

Suave and handsome, he was wearing well-cut dark trousers and a white silk shirt, open at the chest. Very island-ish!

There was a rustle as a steel band began to play music with an exciting beat to it. Over the rim of her glass Jade's eyes met his and sensing a very positive physical reaction towards him she dropped her lashes.

'This must be Sega music,' she said, without looking up. 'Is it?'

'Yes. Later we will dance to it.' The tone of his voice was slightly mocking.

Laughing a little, she looked up at him. 'I can't dance the Sega.'

'You don't have to. They will switch to dance music as you know it, but I think you should give the Sega a try. Expertly, and without fuss, guests are taught the Sega on the dance floor next to the pool.'

'Well,' she glanced down at her drink, 'I'll have to see.' To change the conversation she commented, 'Nicole seems to be kept very busy. The moment we stepped into the clinic people started clamouring for her attention. She looked quite harassed.'

'She is very busy,' he replied. 'Into the bargain, she has to travel constantly, to the many clinics she owns, but you know, although Nicole rises early and goes to bed very late, no one has ever seen her look haggard.'

Laughing a little, she said, 'You mentioned that I looked rested, a moment ago. Did I, then, look haggard on the plane?'

'You looked very beautiful, but upset and very frightened. Perhaps one of the most pleasant things to happen to a man is when he is able to be of some small comfort and assistance to a beautiful girl, and I hope I was of some assistance?' A small, quick smile tugged at his mouth and a shock of excitement raced through her.

'You were, thank you.'

Her silky caftan blew softly about her bare legs and curled itself around her ankles in the breeze which came in from the coral reef, and it was the most sensual sensation.

At that moment the manager came along and introduced himself and introduced her to several people. They all knew Laurent Sevigny, of course, who remained constantly at her side. With his dark, exciting looks and intent eyes, he reminded Jade of the corsairs who had gone before and who had added their names to the history of the island.

When she finally found herself alone with him again he surprised her by saying, 'What were you thinking about, a moment ago, to make you look like that?'

After a startled little pause she said lightly, 'I don't think I should tell you.'

'Why?' By a blink of his lashes she knew that she had made him just more than a little curious.

'You might resent it,' she said. Her hair had fallen partly over her face as she stared down at the glass she was holding and she shook it back and glanced up at him.

'Why is this?' His eyes went over her.

'I was thinking that you must surely be very much the corsair type.'

'I am interested in what you have to say,' he said. 'In what way?'

'Looks, of course.'

'Looks? I must admit that such a thing has never crossed my mind. I've never thought about how a corsair might have looked.'

'Well,' she felt confused now, and slightly ridiculous, 'obviously they were brave—and dashing.'

Beneath the dark stroke of his brows his eyes searched her face, then he laughed.

'There are countless stories and legends about that doubtless interesting and dashing occupation. The pirate was a sea-robber who looted ships, of all nations, including his own. If captured, he was hanged on the spot. The corsair, on the other hand, was a gentleman plunderer who operated under a letter of marque, issued by his own government. This was a document which gave him authority to raid ships of his country's enemies. The corsair did not molest vessels of his own country or its allies. So, in other words, I remind you of a gentleman?' He laughed again and looked at her with amusement. 'A dashing, velvet-hatbox type of gentleman? I do not like this description.'

In a reckless mood she went on, 'What I'm trying to say is that you are dangerously handsome, Monsieur Sevigny. There, that must be the cocktail talking!'

'You are interested in how people look because you are a beauty therapist?'

'How did you know? I don't remember telling you what work I'm to do here. I might have been going to work in the office.'

She watched him as he took her glass and placed it, along with his own, on a passing tray and then, taking fresh drinks, he handed one to her. 'For this work you have a diploma, no?' He ignored her question. 'You received it in London? Before Australia you lived in England. You told me this yourself.'

'Yes, in London.' She could still feel the lingering touch of his fingers on her own as she had taken the glass from him.

For a while they were caught up by people who knew Laurent Sevigny and they remained standing while they nibbled at hot snacks, in between sipping at their drinks and making conversation. Nicole de Spéville arrived but left after barely having sipped at a cocktail.

It was nearing the dining hour and the cocktail party was beginning to break up as guests made their way back to the main section of the hotel.

'Have another cocktail,' said Laurent, looking at Jade, and then without waiting on an answer, he put both their near-empty glasses on a tray and took two full glasses. 'That fragrance you are wearing,' he passed Jade a glass. 'I am completely fascinated by it.'

'Thank you. Wearing a delicious perfume makes me feel far more adventurous than I really am. Quite apart from that, however, it's far more important to me than wearing a piece of superb jewellery.'

'So I notice. I notice, particularly, that you do not even wear an engagement ring, and yet you are here to marry Marlow Lewis.'

Now that most of the people had left the bikini bar the breakers out on the reef sounded very loud.

When Jade answered him there was a note of reservation in the tone of her voice. 'Not yet.' After a moment she asked, 'And you?'

'I am not interested in being faithful to any one particular girl. Life for me has always been a succession of beautiful girls.' She was startled by his abruptness. 'Half the time they mean exactly nothing.'

'I—I suppose it's time to go to dinner,' she said. It was all she could think of.

'Time is no object in Mauritius. But yes, we will dine together, unless you have made other arrangements?'

'I'm glad you added that last bit,' she said, feeling ruffled.

'What do you mean?' he asked.

'Well, to begin with, you made it sound like an order.'

'And that made you fume?' He sounded amused now.

'Yes. Besides, I'd surmised that you would be dining at your chalet.'

'I often dine at the hotel. It reflects the extent of my freedom as a bachelor.'

They dined at a table for two, next to the huge windows which overlooked the lawns, garden and dark, glittering pool. Service was polite and swift. A cluster of pink and crimson hibiscus and dark green foliage lay on the crimson tablecloth. The string band had transferred itself to the pool terrace, just beneath the lounge which was open to the sea breezes. Jade noticed that Laurent Sevigny's strange green eyes were highlighted by the flickering candles. They took a long time eating.

He knew Australia far better than she did and she listened to him talking about pacey Sydney with its Victorian-like, Manchester-like architecture, Paddington with its famous wrought-iron decoration and Perth with its market-style complexes. Some of the tension she had felt at the cocktail party at the bikini pool seemed to dwindle away and fade, although she felt disappointed in him ... and not quite certain what to make of him. And yet, she told herself with good reason, this was ridiculous, for it was not Laurent Sevigny she had come here to marry, but Marlow Lewis. The fact that Laurent was not interested in being faithful to any one particular girl had nothing to do with her.

When they were through with their meal they went out to the pool terrace and although people greeted Laurent his privacy was not encroached upon, and this she could understand, now that he had told her he was part of the hotels group.

A lesson in Sega dancing was causing mirth among the guests.

'Most dancing sessions are ushered in in this way,' Laurent told her while she watched, amused and fascinated, as an exhibition of the erotic dance, which he had explained to her was of African origin, was taking place to the tempo of calypso-style and rhythmical pulsating music.

Taking her fingers in his own he led her to a table for two. The soft wall-lights on the pillars reflected in the shivering and glittering black pool, along with the reflections of the people who were gathered around it. Beyond the pool the palms were etched against the blackness.

'Do you like it?' he asked, when they were seated.

'Yes. It's very exciting—like the music.' Their eyes met.

'This dance,' he told her, 'is practically unchanged from the manner in which the islanders performed it in the eighteenth century. It dates from the times of slavery—a mixture of yesterday and today. It is like a cry from the soul, I think.'

'Yes. It's certainly very—spontaneous ... very natural,' she replied.

'Be prepared to take part. It will be expected of you, eventually—though perhaps not as spontaneous and certainly without such abandonment.' Without warning, he reached for her hand and held it on the table in front of him and she could feel the beating of her heart.

On the dance floor, level with the pool, people were joining in, a little self-consciously at first, so far as the new arrivals were concerned.

Still holding her hand, Laurent looked round for one of the bar stewards.

'I've already had so many cocktails,' Jade protested,

'and then wine with dinner.'

'Tonight we are celebrating,' he told her.

'What are we celebrating?' she asked.

'That remains to be seen.' He turned to give her a mocking glance.

At the far end of the lounge two barmen were busy dispensing drinks while several people sat around on high stools, but here, where they were, stewards were taking orders at the tables and service was a little slow.

Later Laurent asked her to dance, and when he took her into his arms she knew that the attraction she felt for him was real.

'You are shivering.' He held her away from him and looked into her eyes. 'Are you cold?' He sounded amazed that this might be the case, for it was very warm.

'No. Maybe I'm just nervous,' she added on an impulse.

His eyes held hers with sudden intensity. 'Why are you nervous?'

She thought frantically for a moment. 'Well, they could stop playing this night-club shuffle kind of music and break into another Sega, couldn't they?'

'And it would make you nervous to dance with me with such complete abandonment, is that it?'

Her thoughts were in a muddle. 'I wouldn't know where to begin,' she confessed.

'I think you ought to know that I am attracted to you,' he said, brushing his lips across her forehead.

'And I think you need to be reminded that I'm here to be married,' she retorted. What was it he had said? *Half the time they mean exactly nothing.* Moodily, she gazed about her. Well, it was obvious that many beautiful girls frequented this island on holiday, apart from the girls who lived in Mauritius.

'And yet he is not here to welcome you?'

'He had to go away. I knew that.'

'Perhaps you need to be reminded, yourself, that you are here to be married? I am hoping that to be the case. Maybe you have forgotten.'

'I'd thought about it. Apart from everything, I should be preparing for tomorrow at the health clinic —not dancing the night away here, like some tourist.' Suddenly she realised the stupidity of all this and was a little annoyed, but she tried not to let him see this. She did not want him to know that he had succeeded in ruffling her.

'If you find yourself thinking about these things,' he held her closer, 'it could be that you find yourself attracted to me?'

'We are being frivolous,' she said, 'at somebody's expense.'

'You mean—Marlow Lewis?' His voice was hard.

'You know I mean Marlow Lewis. The music has stopped,' she added, when he continued to hold her close. 'I must thank you. You saved me from eating by myself.'

'Nicole, of course, did not ask you to dine at her house.' He made it sound as if he knew why.

'I didn't expect her to,' she replied quickly, trying to hide the fact that she had, in fact, expected something like this and was disappointed in Nicole de Spéville.

'No?'

'No.'

'I'll see you to your door,' he told her, and escorted her there. The staircase and corridor which led to it were also open to the sea breezes and island scents.

Plants with huge green leaves growing in white urns cast black shadows on the white walls.

When he took her into his arms he said, very softly, 'I am feeling my way with you. That, of course, must be obvious to you.'

His breathing felt tight. 'It is,' she said, 'very obvious, and I can tell you right now, this is a mistake with you.'

'I don't think so.' Placing his fingers beneath her chin, he raised her lips to his own. Moving her head slightly, Jade said, 'I promised myself a long time ago, Laurent, not to allow any man to feel his way with me. I should imagine you must have a very bad reputation on this island.'

Laughing a little, but sounding irritated, nevertheless, he said, 'A very bad reputation with women, you mean?'

'Yes.'

'I'm too smart for that,' he told her. When he kissed her she went weak for a moment and then her body was seized by excitement. 'Goodnight,' he said, releasing her, and, humiliated, Jade watched him go.

CHAPTER THREE

BIRDS came to perch on the railing of her balcony in the morning and then, seeking food, hopped down on the glass topped table. The setting was perfect ... the sun, the coral reef, lush foliage and the exciting promise of sheer contentment.

Wearing only a bronze silk pyjama jacket and bikini

pants, Jade went to stand there. Her legs were tanned and beautiful and her dark hair seemed streaked with golden lights.

To one side of the hotel and forming a part of it was the glass-fronted health clinic ... a self-contained haven of tranquillity with its own private terrace.

Inside her room the radio was playing, for she had turned it on before coming out on to the balcony, and it seemed both romantic and fitting that the tune being played was *The Way We Were*, reminding her of the flight and of Laurent Sevigny.

'The staff ratio is high,' Nicole de Spéville's secretary had written to Jade. 'We have on our staff dieticians, two nursing Sisters, several electrologists and trained physio-technologists and two beauticians. At the moment, however, we have only one beautician and eagerly await your arrival. There is also a unisex hair-dressing salon, a masseur and doctor of chiropractics and osteopathy. Comtesse de Spéville's brother, Yves Mézery, is in charge of the men's section.'

Jade decided to have a quick swim before showering and eating breakfast and, going back into the air-conditioned room, she slipped into a maillot, which was supposed to be replacing the bikini and which was a far cry from the Annette Kellerman one-piece intro-duced in 1900. Later she left the pool, glistening bronze in the drying sun, and ate a breakfast of tropical fruit at a table overlooking the sea.

Nicole was in her office when she went along to the clinic and looked up as Jade entered. The caftan she was wearing was a soft, almost sexy, creation in flimsy silk. 'Ah, Jade. Sit down, please. We must fit you for uniforms which you can see, of course, are all in our particular shade of hibiscus-pink.' Her eyes went briefly over Jade's white slacks and striped blouse. 'I was sorry I could not be with you last night, but I was very tired. However,' the blue eyes changed expression very slightly, 'you were with the handsome Laurent Sevigny, were you not?'

'Yes, I was.'

'You appear—attracted to him?'

'I hardly know him.' Jade found herself on the defensive. 'I only met him on the plane.'

'Well, certainly he appeared attracted to you, but then I cannot blame him. You are very beautiful and he has an eye for beauty.'

'I've come here to marry Marlow Lewis,' Jade tried to keep her voice light and teasing. 'Or had you forgotten?'

'No, that I had not forgotten.' Nicole's voice sounded suddenly angry. She stood up. 'Well, let's get you settled in.'

As they walked in the direction of the salon in which Jade was to work Nicole said, 'When Marlow spoke to me about you I was worried, not having met you. You had the qualifications, yes, but I go a lot on the quality I look for when I interview somebody I am going to employ. I was reluctant to allow the fact that you were coming here to Mauritius to marry Marlow influence my decision. I can see, however, that you have the quality I look for.'

'What is that quality, Nicole?' Jade found she did not know what to make of Nicole de Spéville, for while the Comtesse seemed friendly enough there was a kind of abruptness about her.

'It is that ability which makes people feel at ease, and I feel you possess this gift which is an integral part to the salon atmosphere.'

After a moment Jade said, 'I've always enjoyed my work. It helps, I suppose. I find the work fascinating because I like people. One thing I have learned is that beneath the face I'm treating there's a woman who is looking for the security of knowing that she can be more beautiful, more ...' she shrugged, 'desirable, if she can only be taught how to regain more confidence in herself. It's up to me to bring out this beauty, after all, and to reveal to her that she can be very beautiful, if she knows how to work on herself after she's through with me.'

Unlike her staff, who were wearing various shades of hibiscus-pink, Nicole was wearing one of her favourite caftans of black organdie with handpainted sunflowers and green leaves on it, and it floated about her hard, slim body as she moved. The garment seemed so much a part of the island, Jade found herself thinking.

'This way,' said Nicole. Written in gold lettering across one window in the arcade were the words Comtesse Nicole de Spéville, Institut de Beauté. Behind them the area was tastefully dressed. Shaded hibiscus-pink, apricot, gold and cinnamon chiffon had been carefully draped to accommodate a long string of gleaming pearls. Next to the chiffon was a huge flacon of perfume and more pearls in an open black shell. Two brilliant blue Foo Temple dogs were reflected in an antique mirror.

'I think you will enjoy working in this glamorous place,' said Nicole, and Jade's excited eyes flickered round the reception area of the salon, which they had just entered. This section of the salon was decorated with ancient Chinese, Japanese and Indian furniture. Carved temple good-luck charms were adorned with hibiscus-red Persian silk cushions which contrasted magnificently with the black wood.

Glancing about her, Nicole said, 'I bought these chairs from Laurent Sevigny,' and, at the sound of the name, Jade's senses quickened.

'They're absolutely beautiful,' she said, a little breathlessly.

'According to Laurent,' Nicole went on, 'they bear all the carvings of the ancient Chinese designs on them ... phoenix, lotus and temple dragon.'

'He sounds like an expert on the subject,' Jade answered.

'Yes, he is, but then he needs to be.' Nicole's bright blue eyes were on Jade's face, and then she said, 'Look at this exotic bronze dragon incense burner, and over here on this carved base is a brass incense burner. I put them all in here. To me it is worth it, for it brings glamour to the Salon.'

'It's very exciting,' Jade replied, her thoughts on the exciting Laurent Sevigny who had made it perfectly clear that he was 'feeling his way with her'.

'Over here ...' said Nicole, 'a Japanese cabinet. In it, as you can see, flacons of perfume from France ... all with their gold cords. The perfume is sensuous and mysterious and I must let you have some as a gift. I happen to know that Laurent is attracted to it.'

'And—Marlow?' Jade felt it her duty to say.

'Ah ... Marlow.' Nicole was silent for a moment and then went on, 'The paintings are my own. It is my way of relaxing. Marlow, of course, is a sculptor.'

Jade's eyes widened. 'Marlow—a sculptor? I didn't know that.' The idea that the tough Marlow was a sculptor completely surprised her, just as the fact that he was a hunter had shocked her.

Turning, Nicole said, 'I am surprised. You didn't

know this? That the man you are here to marry carves in his spare time?'

'No.' Jade was somewhat put out at the accusation in Nicole's voice. 'It's just—well, on the sheep station Marlow didn't carve, that's for sure ... I mean,' she found herself floundering, 'I didn't see him carve anything. He seems so—hard—to be bothered about fiddling round with sculpture, that's all.'

'Marlow is very sensitive. The craft of wood-carving has literally become a part of his nature, setting him free to express his thoughts, which is one of the rewards of the life of a sculptor—or an artist.' Nicole's voice still held accusation.

After a moment Jade said, 'And yet Marlow hunts. He hunts down animals.'

'What has that to do with it?' Nicole's voice sounded slightly harsh now. 'As a hunter Marlow is well-known on the island. As a sculptor he is becoming well known in certain circles.'

'Well, fine.' Jade allowed the fact that she was peeved to show. 'That's just fine with me. I'm pleased he's becoming well know through something as beautiful as wood-carving.'

'Let us get back to the reason as to why we are here,' Nicole said shortly. 'Already, Jade, there is a waiting list for you ... the beautician from London.'

'That's nice to know.' Jade's eyes went to the wide Moorish arch beyond which was the hairdressing salon. Several women sat under dryers, reading. To one side was the restful, rose-tinted mirrored and dimly lit salon where facials took place; the waxing, eyelash implants, manicures and pedicures.

The day was progressing. She was fitted for the hibiscus-pink shifts she would have to wear and then, selecting one 'off the peg' to go on with, she went back to her room overlooking the coral reef and changed into it, ready for her first facial. Then she ate lunch on the terrace, immediately in front of the clinic, and when Laurent Sevigny spoke she almost jumped and looked up at him through tinted lenses, characteristically shaking back her hair. 'Oh, hello,' she said, confused.

'I am surprised to find you eating here,' he said, 'for you, of course, cannot possibly be on a diet. You are too slim for that.' His eyes went over her.

'I—er—keep to a diet, for all that,' she found herself stammering, in view of what had taken place outside her door, the night before, and the fact that as she responded to his kisses he had humiliated her by releasing her and walking away.

'What *is* that?' He sounded amused. 'A stuffed tomato?'

'Yes. I could have had fish and a salad,' she glanced at three women, wearing short pink robes supplied by Nicole, who had chosen this for lunch, 'but I didn't feel like it.' She watched him as he pulled a chair from the table and sat down opposite her.

'Why are you eating here, in any case,' he asked, 'and not in the main section of the hotel? You are not a client.'

'I will take my breakfast here, and my lunch.' She wondered what he was doing here.

'I was looking for you.' He spoke with characteristic authority.

'Oh?' She tried to keep her voice polite, nothing more, and turned away from that strange green gaze of his to look at people splashing about in the pool. The French instructor was calling out instructions to a tall girl with flaming red hair and piped music was being carried away on the sea-breezes. The fronds of palm trees rattled and the sigh of filao trees could be heard.

Laurent's eyes went to Jade's legs which she had crossed to one side of the table, as she intended to sit back now and sip her pineapple juice. When she moved them slightly he said, 'No, don't move them. I was admiring your smooth gold tan.'

'From the Australian sun,' she told him. 'I'm off to a good start. At least I didn't arrive on your heavenly island looking like a pale ghost.'

'It is a logical conclusion,' he said, his eyes on her face again, 'that you are completely rested and settled in.'

'As you can see....' she bowed her head, and kept her voice light. Then she watched his tanned fingers go to the hibiscus which was arranged on the table. He touched the blooms without knowing that he was doing it.

'Do you see what is written on the card?' Jade asked, mainly to make conversation.

'I know about that,' he said, barely glancing at the ornate gold lettering which read: Please do not eat the hibiscus. 'What I am interested in is—what time do you finish here?'

'Finish here?' She sounded frankly amused. 'I finish here late this afternoon—fiveish, I believe.'

'After which time you are free to do as you wish.' It was a statement, more than anything else.

'Well, yes. As I *wish*.' She placed emphasis on the word, in an endeavour to make it clear that her wish was not that she be the victim of his 'feeling his way' with her.

'I am having a few people to my chalet for drinks,' he

told her. 'I want you to be there.'

Although her reaction was one of swift excitement it was followed by anger. 'You make it sound like an order,' she commented.

'I have learned one thing,' his smile was faintly mocking, 'that when a woman shows anger, it is because she is tempted. I will come for you before anyone else arrives.'

'That's nonsense,' she retorted. She watched him lift the card and study it. 'And did you,' he asked, 'eat any of the hibiscus?'

'No,' she said shortly. 'I'm very switched off by hibiscus. I don't eat them. I get high on yellow roses, though.'

'In that case, I will see to it that you are supplied with yellow roses every day. You, of course, are an English rose, although you are tanned by the Australian sun. At the moment you do not look very English.'

'No?' She shook her dark hair from her cheeks.

'No. You look very much a part of our island in the sun.' He stood up. 'I will call for you, Jade.'

'How do you know I'll come?' She looked up at him.

'Because the idea of having drinks at my pink chalet enchants you ... among other things.'

'You don't have to call for me,' she said, 'I can walk there. After all, it's not far ... merely a walk beneath the palms and through the hibiscus with paving stones to guide me, all the way.'

'So?' He smiled down at her. 'You have already found this out for yourself?'

'You pointed it out to me,' she said quickly, and felt her cheeks flush, because she had, in fact, found this out for herself ... before lunch.

He went on looking down at her, green-eyed and considering, and she got the faint drift of sandalwood spray cologne for men.

'I'll—I'll be in the lounge, just off the pool,' she told him, 'and what time—seven?'

'Six-thirty,' he said. 'I want you to myself for a while.'

Jade went back to her woman's world of masses of silk and fine cotton curtaining in shades of hibiscus-pinks, apricot and cinnamon-gold, plunge-pools, avacado-green tiles and subterranean sounds, saunas, towels and powder, beautiful Creole girls trained in the art of massage, arches and louvred doors and exotic potted plants, and her mind was full of Laurent Sevigny.

The salon she was to work in offered tranquillity with its rose-tinted mirrors and subdued lighting.

Although she had performed this kind of work in London and, for a short time, in Australia, there was a touch of unreality in it now. It was difficult to believe that she was on this island with its vivid sunsets, palms, beautiful beaches and the sea almost every colour in the palette, depending on the mood of the weather. What was even more difficult was the fact that she had come to the island to marry Marlow Lewis, a man she hardly knew. After her marriage it had been arranged by them in their letters that she would keep on with her work as a beauty therapist.

While she continued to work with oils and creams her mind kept flitting away to Laurent Sevigny. At the moment the upturned face of her client was very still, the eyes closed. Like most women who had booked in at a plush health clinic, she was alone, although, from what Jade had gathered, there were a number of couples with weight, health or tension problems who were making this their holiday at the hydro. Suddenly the lips moved. 'That's heavenly,' the woman said. 'Do you know, you have a marvellous touch?' The eyes remained closed.

'Thank you,' Jade murmured politely. 'I'm pleased you're enjoying your facial.'

'In fact, I'm enjoying my entire stay here. I *did* have a slight weight problem, but nothing serious.' The eyelashes fluttered. 'What I did need, though, was human warmth and contact. My marriage is cracking up and I decided to get away. I hopped on a plane and came here. I'd heard so much about it. You see, I married a man so much older than myself.'

Jade felt herself tensing at the words.

'He's become so—so set in his ways. I notice it more than ever now that the children are teenagers. I was just thinking a moment ago as you worked on my face that your kind of work is unique, really, because you're working with—well, let's say *unique* material—that is, human material. I guess we all have problems—the women who come here. Some of them are lucky—they come with their husbands and make it a kind of holiday, but not all of us are so fortunate. However, at the end, I guess you could say we go back to whatever it is we've left, ready to cope again.'

'You should go back feeling much more relaxed,' said Jade. 'That should help.' She did not know what to say, but in any case, she thought, she was here to listen, after all.

While she went on working and, in view of what her client had told her, she thought about Marlow. After the plane crash in which Jeffrey and Elisa had been killed, she and Marlow had turned to one another for consolation. She could see that now. When Marlow stated that he wanted to quit Australia for Mauritius, she had felt sheer despair and loneliness, and then he had written from the island, asking her to marry him, and with her grief and loneliness to guide her, she had written back, accepting. At a later date Marlow had mentioned the clinic and had suggested that she might well like to work there. Comtesse Nicole de Spéville, he had written, looked forward to her application. Well, she had made application and here she was, to find that Marlow was away on a business trip. He had written to say that he was going away to a sugar congress and unfortunately would be away at the very time she arrived in Mauritius.

While she dressed for drinks at Laurent's chalet she felt frustrated and disturbed because she could not visualise Marlow while she tried to think about him.

When Laurent Sevigny joined her in the open-air lounge he said, 'I find you very beautiful.' His strange green eyes went over the white spaghetti-strapped frock and sandals she was wearing. 'Does that disturb you?'

'Well ...' she hunted around in her mind for something flighty to say in order to show him that she didn't really care one way or another. 'I don't look visibly upset, do I?' She laughed lightly. 'I suppose every girl likes to appear beautiful. On the whole, though, I'm reserved to flattery.'

'I was paying you a compliment,' he told her. 'It is an accepted part of the gallant, velvet-hatbox type of gentleman, I believe.' His eyes mocked her.

'How did your day go?' he asked, as they walked in the direction of his chalet.

'Very well, actually. I'm very excited about everything.'

'Even your forthcoming marriage to the great hunter Marlow Lewis?'

Deciding to ignore his remark, Jade stopped walking to say, 'Don't those clouds look hand-tinted? It's all so beautiful. It's a wonderful island.'

'And yet,' he sounded sad, 'there is poverty on the island as well.'

'I couldn't help noticing all those starving dogs on our way from the airport,' she said, shuddering a little. 'I was quite horrified. Why don't they *do* something about it?'

'Unfortunately,' he said, taking her fingers in his own, '... mind, this paving stone is uneven ... the island is overrun with wretched and mangy dogs.'

'But,' she cut in, to try to calm her fluttering fingers in his, 'why don't they *do* something?'

'You are an impatient young thing,' he said. 'I was coming to that. The Hindu religion forbids the taking of life.'

'I see. I wondered.' His fingers were warm and held hers very firmly and she glanced down at them. 'Some ...' she swallowed and looked up again, 'of the dogs appeared to be dying on their feet, with absolutely no hope.'

'Do not trouble yourself with this problem now.' He gave her a sideways glance. 'I went into Curepipe after I left you today.' He pronounced it Kuur-peep. 'That is where I have my business.'

'Apart from the hotel business, you mean?' Jade asked.

'Yes. I must take you there—also to my house on another part of the island.'

'I'm afraid I'm going to be too busy at the hotel to gad about,' she told him, thinking of Marlow and why she was here.

'In other words you are bothered by being seen about

with me?' He sounded angry.

'Well....' They had reached the double-storey chalet now, which along with several other chalets sat on green lawns with gardens in the coconut grove which fringed the curving white beach.

'Forget the games,' he said curtly. 'The man you have come to marry will have to resign himself to the fact that he is older than you by twenty years and that other men are going to find you desirable and seek your company.' He stopped walking suddenly, and took her in his arms. 'I'll show you what I mean.'

'Don't!' she said sharply, while he continued to look into her eyes with an intensity which she found unnerving.

'Don't what?' His eyes went to her mouth and then, very slowly, tantalisingly almost, he put his lips on hers. Against her will her hands went to his shoulders and she felt the sudden need to press her body against his.

'And you feel you really *know* yourself,' he said, against her lips. 'You know what it is you want—and that is to marry this Marlow Lewis?'

'I *hope* I know myself.' She pulled away from him and he made no attempt to hold her back.

'It is time you cleared up these things,' he told her.

'I think you have a nerve!' She felt angry and humiliated now. 'This puts me in quite another mood. I was feeling happy before, and now....'

'Now you are confused and uncertain, is that it? That comfortable feeling has gone, no?'

'If it has, what satisfaction has it brought you?' she asked.

'Why fight me?' he asked. 'But come, don't look so

serious. I want you to relax. That is why I have invited you here.'

Like the hotel, his chalet was air-conditioned and had magnificent views across the sea-lagoon and ocean, beyond the reef. It was simply furnished with lightly-scaled bamboo and wicker Chinese tables and chairs, with comfortably upholstered cushions, and the ceiling was high and made of timber, stained a light golden shade.

'It's beautiful,' said Jade. 'These very high fan-backed chairs are called peacock chairs, aren't they?'

'When I am in a tropical environment,' said Laurent, 'I want to feel it. But for all that, my house is quite different from this chalet. In this chalet I would have been quite happy to live in the rooms without any furniture at all. The proportions of the rooms are excellent and the windows expertly placed to frame the views. What more can I wish for? All I can think of when I live here is that it is the way I often like to live —light and airy and with a sense of being part of the environment I happen to be in.'

Jade's eyes scanned the few highly personalised objects, books and memorabilia placed casually among the simplified furnishings. 'It's all very nice,' she agreed.

Taking her by the arm he said, 'I hold parties upstairs, in what I call a studio, for want of a better word. My guests know where to come, so we will go upstairs now.'

Suddenly their eyes met. 'What time are your guests coming?' she asked, regarding him with distrust and disappointment.

'We will just have time to enjoy a drink together,' he

told her. 'What is the matter?' She noticed the quirk to his mouth.

'As if you didn't know,' she said, 'but in any case, I've formed a good many disagreeable impressions over a very short period.' This was the time of the day, she was thinking, when his eyes obviously began to change colour ... from that exciting dark sea-green to malachite, almost. With his dark skin smoothly tanned it was an unusual combination.

Suddenly he laughed. 'Come,' he said. 'Have you forgotten that I am a velvet-hatbox gentleman?'

It was obviously a room where people stood around in groups talking, overlapping on to the balcony with its cane and wicker chairs and a vivid assortment of cushions. There was a bar at one end of the studio. The whole area was an exciting backdrop for casual entertaining to solitary sun worship.

'Go out to the balcony while I mix you a drink,' Laurent said easily, and then, later, he came to stand next to her. As Jade took the cocktail from him she said, 'Thank you—how delightfully chilled the glass is. Is this one of your island cocktails?'

'Try it,' he told her. 'I am sure you will like it.'

While he watched her she took a sip. 'Mmmm ... excellent. I notice that every chalet has the most glorious view, including yours, of course. You're very fortunate.'

'Island and paradise are words that go together,' he said. 'My life here happens to be an excellent demonstration of this cliché. I do consider myself to be very fortunate, believe me.'

The tide was pounding the reef, but the sea lagoon was very still and everything seemed to be bathed in a translucent mauve light. Two small fishing vessels reflected their lanterns which wavered on the mauveish water.

'Here,' Laurent was saying, 'I can eat by candlelight, in formal dignity, or I can simply lie around in casual clothes.'

'You talk about eating. Do you cook?' Jade felt a little ridiculous asking this man who looked like a fictional character, with that bold gaze from greenish eyes and sometimes aggressive personality, whether he could cook. 'I—I can't imagine you cooking,' she went on lamely.

'No? And why is this?'

Laughing a little, she said, 'Well, you just don't look the type ... you know, the domesticated type.'

'I have a cook, as it so happens, but I guess I know enough to cook for a chic dinner party ... very small, of course.' While he was speaking she was thinking that part of his sex appeal was the kind of constant mystery he radiated about himself.

'What do you call a *small* dinner party?' she asked.

'For two,' he said. He gave her an almost piratical grin.

From where they were standing on the balcony, they could see the first guests arriving, so she was saved an answer.

'So you like my chalet?' he said.

'Yes, it's most attractive. The view is so beautiful, into the bargain, that my eyes keep going to it.'

'I intend to change that,' he told her. 'The view will not be allowed to monopolise your attention. However, later on you will of course live in a sugar plantation house.' His eyes were suddenly darker. 'That is if you do marry Marlow Lewis.'

'There are no ifs about it. I'm here to marry Marlow.'

'And yet,' his eyes held hers and then went to her mouth, 'the tone of your voice indicates that you have reservations about this.'

'Not at all. That's a ridiculous thing to say!' She laughed lightly, trying to hide the fact that he had ruffled her.

'Come,' he said. 'Unfortunately there is no time to continue with our little discussion on this subject.'

They went back into the large room, which he referred to as a studio and which looked stunning with bowls of flowers and baskets containing jungle orchids. Two young Indian men had already begun to hand out drinks from trays, while another dispersed them behind the bar counter. There were snacks of all varieties.

Laurent Sevigny had apparently invited a small number of carefully selected guests, and the atmosphere was multi-racial and cosmopolitan and very elegantly casual.

Holding a fresh drink between her slim, tanned fingers, Jade found herself being introduced around by Laurent. Whenever she found herself separated from him she stood sipping her island punch and watched him, with fascination, as he talked with people and moved from one group to another. He had complete confidence in himself and appeared highly experienced in his dealings with women, she noticed, and the thought gave her no pleasure.

There was a little rustle as Nicole de Spéville, wearing a black embroidered voile caftan, arrived, and when she saw Jade she left the people she was with and came to stand next to her. 'Hello. I went to your room, after first having tried to get you on the telephone, but you were not there. I wanted to find out what you were doing this evening. I was then told by reception that you had gone with Laurent to his chalet ... and here you are. You appear to be managing very well without Marlow.'

At that moment Laurent joined them. 'I was just saying to Jade,' said Nicole, looking at him, 'that owing to the fact that I feel responsible for her welfare until Marlow arrives back, I rang her room and then went there myself to invite her on your behalf to come here with me. It didn't strike me that you had already done this. A drama is going on here, maybe?'

'Yes—and no.' Laurent laughed shortly, but Jade could see that he was angry.

'You have fallen in love at first sight, maybe?' Nicole's voice was slightly amused, but her eyes were probing.

'Love? That counts for nothing in my estimation.' Laurent spoke carelessly. 'What is love, after all?'

'You seem to be so—friendly,' Nicole went on, 'on such short acquaintance. It just did not strike me that I would find Jade here, although you *have* been seen about.'

'Society has reached a stage where it no longer says no to temptations,' said Laurent. 'On very short acquaintance I was tempted to invite Miss Lawford here, and as you can see for yourself, she was tempted to accept.'

'It seems I've committed a crime by accepting this invitation.' Jade's voice was stiff.

'Well, temptation can only get you into trouble,' said Nicole, and although her voice was amused now, there was an expression in her eyes which Jade could not understand. 'After all, you have come here to marry Marlow, but perhaps you will change your mind, after all?'

'Perhaps she will,' Laurent cut in, 'and perhaps to your advantage, Nicole, no?'

'I have no experience in this sort of cross-talk,' said Jade. 'How am I supposed to act?' She laughed lightly, but she was furious.

Cool and self-assured, confident in the knowledge that she was a beautiful woman, Nicole was very still and said nothing, but her breathing gave her away. 'I am thinking of Marlow,' she said, after a moment, 'who is away right now. I am afraid I cannot stay long. I came here direct from the clinic and I hate driving at night on the island, so ...' she glanced round for a place to set her glass, 'you will excuse me, please. I'll see you in the morning.' She glanced in Jade's direction. 'By the way, did Laurent tell you that he is a collector of jade?'

'Yes, I believe he did mention that,' Jade replied stiffly.

'He is a man of style,' Nicole went on, 'a man who manages to maintain that almost lost art of evoking elegance, don't you think? Even when he is wearing sun-bleached denims and a tee-shirt.'

'And you are given to flights of fancy,' he replied shortly.

'He is also a rich and exacting man,' Nicole said. 'He likes beautiful things.'

When Nicole had gone Laurent said, 'Come out to the balcony. There are not so many people out there.'

'Some of them are preparing to leave,' Jade made no effort to move. 'I must be going too. Thank you for having me.'

'I think Nicole has succeeded in causing you annoyance,' he commented, taking her by the arm.

'And I don't think you're overstating the case,' she

snapped. 'What I do in my leisure hours has nothing to do with her.'

'She has her reasons.' He led her in the direction of the balcony and, curious to hear more, Jade allowed him to get away with it.

On the balcony she said, 'I'm feeling very ruffled. Of course, I was a fool to come here.'

'Nicole is seen at all the fashionable restaurants and night spots on the island. She never stays very long, whether it is at one of these places or a private residence, but she is often outspoken and unpredictable.'

'Contrary to the impression she might have gained, I have no desire to engage in an affair with you,' Jade went on. The fact that she was annoyed spurred her on. 'I've enjoyed seeing your chalet. It's an ideal setting for—a philanderer. Obviously, Nicole resents the fact that I was invited here.'

'There is much you don't understand about Nicole,' he told her.

'And much I have no wish to understand.' While she was speaking Jade was thinking that she was in no position to be critical of the fact that Nicole was so much older than Laurent Sevigny. After all, who was she to criticise when she was here to marry a man who gave her twenty years? 'I must leave now. It's getting on for dinner time.'

'Are you hungry?' he asked.

'Hardly. You put up an excellent spread for a cocktail party,' she replied, wanting to leave and yet wanting to stay here with him. 'I was trying to work out what some of those curried savouries were.'

'Samoosas,' he said. His eyes never left her face. He seemed to be saying things automatically, without thinking. 'You mean the thin pastry envelopes filled with curried meat and diced potatoes, of course?'

'Yes.'

'So you believe that this is the place of a philanderer?'
He went on looking at her. 'How can you be so sure?'

'You've given me all the proof I need,' she replied.
'You're a class of your own.'

'Oh?' His voice was cool. 'And how do you explain
that?'

'Well, it's quite obvious that if anyone ever gets
hurt, it certainly wouldn't be you, for one thing.'

'I have hurt you, then?' He was slightly mocking.

'I was not talking about me. It has nothing to do
with me what you do.'

'And yet it rattles you?' He laughed softly. 'Come,'
he said, 'let us not get into deep water. I want you to
stay on, and after everybody has gone, we will listen to
music ... and I will mix you a very special drink, with
fruit at the bottom of the glass and decorating the side
of it, and later we will have something to eat.' She
watched him moodily as he lifted a hand in farewell to
someone who was leaving.

'I don't think so,' she answered.

'And why is that?' He took her fingers in his own.

'Because is could bring disorder.'

'Disorder does not bother me.' He lifted her hand to
his lips.

'But it bothers me.' Jade wriggled them free.

'You are acting as though I have just asked you to
spend a weekend with me,' he drawled, and the remark
caused her immediate humiliation. 'Whereas,' he continued, 'I have merely asked you to stay on, enjoy some
music, have another drink and, later, eat a meal prepared for us by my very excellent cook. Soon after
coffee and a liqueur, maybe, I will see you back to the

hotel ... all very casual.'

'So casual, in fact, that my presence here caused Nicole de Spéville to be jealous? And no doubt there are others.'

'I don't understand this,' he said. 'Why are you troubling yourself with these thoughts? Are you jealous because you believe Nicole is jealous?'

'Of course not! Why should I be jealous?'

'So, as this makes no difference to you ... that is what Nicole or any woman might feel because you have dined with me here, there is no reason why you should not stay. Okay?' Suddenly he smiled, and the hand that writes on the wall was beginning to write something else for her.

'Okay,' she found herself saying, 'it's just that Nicole seemed to be trying to get something across to me and I found myself resenting her remarks.'

'There is nothing to prevent you from doing as you please,' he told her. 'You are not married to Marlow Lewis yet. As for Nicole, she is very unhappy.'

'Who is responsible for this unhappiness?' she asked. 'Or shouldn't I ask?'

'That is something I am not prepared to discuss with you.'

Laurent's guests were in various stages of departing and then suddenly they were alone and they went downstairs, and Jade watched him moodily as he mixed her an island cocktail. After he had frosted the rim of the glass with what appeared to be caster sugar he passed it to her.

'What are you brooding about?' His strange green eyes went over her face. The glass doors were open to the lawns and they could hear the breakers on the coral reef.

'I wasn't brooding,' she lied, feeling something like 'the girl who just can't say no.' 'I was admiring the beautiful objects in your chalet, as a matter of fact.'

'I come from a long line of collectors,' he told her. 'I myself am a collector. Many of the things I like to collect speak of a bygone age. I suppose collecting is in my blood.'

'Isn't this what is called a Foo dog?' she asked, reaching out finger-tips to touch the blue-and-white, ferocious-looking dog.

'Yes. To be precise, it is a hand-painted Kutani Foo dog.' He gave her a smile which, for her, cast him in a hero mould from which, so far as she was concerned, he would never escape, and that was the dashing, swordplaying corsair type. 'When I take you to my house I will show you the jade phoenix.'

'Did I say anything about visiting your house?' Jade kept her voice light. While he had been speaking she had been reminding herself that he was a man who would collect women. This, too, would be in his blood and in the end they, too, would speak of a bygone age. The only difference was that they would no longer grace his chalet, or the house he had told her about previously.

'Looking at you,' he ignored her question, 'I can see that you have a style which can only be described as an expression of your individuality. It would be almost impossible for anyone to copy Jade Lawford.'

'Your description of me comes as a surprise. You mentioned to Nicole that she was given to flights of fancy. It seems to me that you are also given to flights of fancy.' Suddenly Jade felt trapped in the magnificent peacock-shaped wicker chair with its vivid blue silk cushion. 'I think I prefer to think of myself as elegant rather than stylish.'

'No, you are stylish,' he replied, 'and you carry this stylishness to the ultimate. In any case, the two are closely knit ... style and elegance.'

Feeling inclined to argue with him, to show him that his very personal remarks did not affect her, she said, 'I should say that elegance is—is very static. *I* am static.'

'If you were static, you would not be here.' He spoke the words slowly, with emphasis. 'However, you are elegant and very beautiful and you *do* have style, and that alone must surely demand that you devote yourself to certain changes, whether you are aware of this, or not. Style goes hand in hand with a shifting nature, no? Therefore, as I see it, style can be so much more rewarding than elegance or just good taste.'

She took a sip of her cocktail and looked at him over the rim of her glass. 'Oh? In what way?'

'Style, I believe, is constantly searching for perfection, whereas elegance, on the other hand, can only bring about a tranquil pleasure.'

'Well, is that such a bad thing?' She wished he would not look at her in that cool appraising manner.

'Yes, it is very bad. Style explores everything there is to explore. I don't think you are complacent, and derive pleasure only from a feeling of tranquillity. You wouldn't be here with me now if you did. Think about this while I go and tell Capauelle what to prepare for us. We'll eat on the balcony. The studio will have been cleared of the remnants of the cocktail party, by the time the meal is ready.'

Moodily Jade watched him leave the room. There was a kind of autocracy in all his movements. In his presence she felt seductive and, what was more, submissive, and knowing this, she realised that she was treading on dangerous ground. In a cold and exciting light, she saw herself as his victim—and hated herself for it.

How many women, she wondered later when they were on the balcony which led off the studio, and as she surveyed the round table with its billowing voile cloth, posy of flowers and candles flickering in the breeze, had stayed on with Laurent Sevigny, alone, after one of his cocktail parties? The drink he had mixed for her downstairs, and the perfectly chilled wine she was drinking now with the well-prepared if light meal, did nothing to melt her apprehension.

'Why do you look at me like that?' he asked suddenly. His dark green eyes did not leave her face.

'I was just thinking. . . .' She searched around in her mind for something flippant to say. 'I like to read in the evenings, and here I am, acting like a millionaire's daughter on an island vacation. Do you realise I have to work tomorrow?'

'But the following day you are free.'

'How did you know that?' She widened her eyes at him.

'I took time off to find out. The day after tomorrow is your free day and that is the day we are going to Curepipe.'

'You go on as if I have no say at all,' she said crossly.

'Don't you respect masculine power?' he asked.

'Yes, I do, but not when it's directed at me.'

'And how do you aim to stop it?' He held his glass to the candle light and studied it.

'Since you have no power over me I don't have to try. You really are very sure of yourself, aren't you?'

'Certainly I recognise a certain reluctance,' his voice was easy, 'but I am of the opinion that you are very much aware of the fact that I am reasonably sure of myself.'

Deliberately, Jade raised her glass to her lips. 'Let me cue you again,' she said, after she had taken a sip of her wine. 'Soon I'll be the wife of a sugar farmer on this island.'

'Since you didn't question the foolishness of dining alone with me in my chalet in his absence,' he said, 'I gather this is of little importance to you.' His eyes were mocking now.

'I *did* question it,' she protested.

'And yet here you are.' He laughed very softly.

'Yes, here I am, and I've probably given rise to a whole lot of gossip.'

'Gossip doesn't bother me,' he answered. 'One day before Marlow gets back we will go on a champagne picnic. I will take you to a place where we will enjoy a superb Chinese meal, afterwards, in the authentic atmosphere ... and where we will be seen.'

'Many things appear not to bother you,' she observed.

'I'll admit that is the case.' He sat back and studied her.

After the meal they went downstairs again to listen to music and sat on plump cushions which Laurent had carelessly thrown on to the carpet. When he bent his head to kiss her her lips were more than willing and she knew that her trials with Laurent Sevigny were only just beginning. As her arms went around his neck she was quite resigned to the possibility of becoming yet another helpless victim. He kissed her sensuously and, once, while she opened her eyes to look into his face, the expression in his strange green eyes seemed to darken, as he made his calculations about her. What

was it he'd said ... 'I'm not interested in being faithful to any one particular girl.'

And yet who was she to set such high standards?
she thought, as a feeling of humiliation surged over her.

'Let go of me!' She struggled away from him.

'You enjoy being kissed by me, no?'

'Yes, but only for the simple reason that I've possibly
had too many of your island cocktails and wine and because I must have taken leave of my senses. There!
Now are you satisfied?'

'It takes a lot to satisfy me,' he answered. 'But come,
I will take you back to the hotel now.'

A mask seemed to have been fitted over his dark
handsome face, hiding his thoughts. It was as though
he had been watching a very boring play which had
held absolutely no interest for him.

On the way back to the hotel, Jade stumbled on a
paving stone which was set into the lawn, but although
Laurent caught her to him, he made no attempt to kiss
her.

CHAPTER FOUR

WHEN her phone rang the following afternoon Jade
was in her room and, as she was new to the island, her
eyes widened. She knew that it wasn't Nicole, for
Nicole had left the clinic for her house on the slopes of
one of those fantastically shaped mountains. Perhaps, she
thought a little wildly, it was Marlow who had arrived
back earlier than intended.

It was Laurent Sevigny. 'Right now, what are you

doing?' he asked. 'I know that you are finished at the salon, of course.'

'Right now,' she said, after a moment and in a tight little voice, 'I'm preparing to swim in the pool.'

'You are most welcome to use my pool at the chalet,' he told her.

'The hotel pool will suit me fine—but thank you, all the same.'

'About last night——' he began.

'I don't want to talk about it.'

'Do you not wish to see Curepipe?' Jade knew he was mocking her. 'We did not discuss it before we parted and so I have phoned to make arrangements. We will leave soon after we have eaten breakfast together.'

She allowed a long, astonished breath to escape her lips. 'You're not dictating to a person of limited intelligence,' she said hotly. 'Really, I decide these things for myself! As for breakfast .... well, I'm now making it a practice to eat breakfast here in my room every day, in common with some of the clients at the health clinic. I think you're looking at things from off-centre, don't you?'

'No,' he replied easily. 'It is my intention to change this routine, so far as tomorrow is concerned. I'll meet you at eight at the hotel.' Suddenly, his laugh came to her. 'Oh, come, Jade. You are in a petty and quarrelsome mood.' When she made no reply he said, 'What is wrong with going to Curepipe?'

'There's nothing wrong with going to Curepipe,' she answered.

'Okay, so we go. Tomorrow, then.'

After he had rung off she stood looking down at the receiver and then slowly put it down.

She thought about Laurent while she swam in the

pool and again as she showered and changed for dinner. There was no sign of him in the dining-room, although she searched for him with her eyes, and later again in the lounge, which was open to the sea breezes and the pool. Later she danced with an Australian she had been introduced to and he stirred those memories of Australia that were always moving about in her mind.

That night she cried into her pillow—for Jeffrey and for Elisa, who had been engaged to Marlow. Why, she asked herself, had Marlow written to ask her to marry him? And why had she accepted him? Was it because they had both suffered a tragic loss? Had he ended up feeling pity for her after he had simply sold his sheep station in Australia and gone to Mauritius, leaving her to make fresh plans for herself now that the place that had been home to herself and Jeffrey no longer belonged to the man who had been Jeffrey's employer? Had her letters conveyed to him the despair she felt, the indecision as to what she should do? There was nothing to go back to in England, she had written to Marlow. She had also written about her new position in a beauty salon and, out of the blue, Marlow had written proposing marriage, and because it had seemed like a good idea she had accepted and here she was, but where Marlow should have been there was the fascinating and devastating Laurent Sevigny. . . .

Tanned and lean and wearing denim jeans, tight across his narrow hips and across his body, and a cotton shirt, open almost to the waist, Laurent was waiting for her the following morning. He looked elegantly casual and he wore the denim wranglers well and she could not take her eyes off him. She saw that he had thrown a denim jacket over one of the poolside chairs.

'You look—very French,' she couldn't resist telling him.

'Like one of the corsairs we discussed?' His dark sea-green eyes were lazy. 'But tell me, what do you mean— I look very French? I *am* French.'

'Oh,' she shrugged, 'I mean you look cool, self-reliant and elegant ... even in wranglers.'

'Well,' he said, and stepped back, his legs apart, and looking down at them, 'I prefer this character you have just invented to the velvet-hatbox type of gentleman, I think. I am starving,' he went on, 'and I hope you are too. I can't stand women who pick at their food.' His voice was very reasonable and made it impossible for her to go on being churlish and childish.

In the dining-room, with its walls of glass on three sides, they helped themselves to fruit ... mangoes, paw-paw, tiny pineapples, which were deliciously and un-believably sweet and cut down the centre, fat yellow bananas, and this was followed by crisp bacon and an omelette. Over coffee Jade said, 'Everything is so blue and so green and gold. The beaches are so white and fine, all perfect foils for the pink oleanders and pink and red hibiscus. Actually, the beach reminds me of a setting for a pirate film scene.'

'Where we are going you won't be able to see over the sugar-cane, which seems to grow extra high in Mauritius.'

'Marlow has written about the high cane,' she said quietly. After a moment she asked, 'Do you know it— Marlow's plantation house?'

'I have been there, yes ... once or twice.'

'I—but I thought you were not a friend of Mar-low's?' She was instantly puzzled.

'I'm not. I went to pick up Nicole who was visiting there.'

'Oh, I see,' she replied, but she didn't see, though she overcame the temptation to ask him what Nicole was doing there.

They walked back to his chalet and his car was parked in front of it, near to the leaning palm which he had previously pointed out as a landmark to her, since the chalets all looked the same.

As he opened the car door for her he said, 'You should be wearing a white lace hat with a cluster of real yellow or pink roses on it.'

When he got in beside her she said, very softly, 'By the way, thank you for the yellow roses you sent along to my room.'

'Did you get high on them?' he asked, turning to look at her, 'like you said you do?'

'They're beautiful,' she said, after a moment.

She was wearing a cinnamon cotton sun-frock with sandals to match and had donned sunglasses which blotted out her dark blue eyes—and most of her pert face, for that matter . . . all very casual and understated, but she knew she looked good. Interesting gold bangles made clinking noises on both wrists when she moved.

'Do you know,' Laurent was saying as he turned the car and made for the driveway which led in the direction of huge white pillars which had black wrought-iron gates fastened back from them, 'there is a flawless and polished but nevertheless casually stated look about you. I should imagine that being a beautician adds to the gift you have of making yourself even more beautiful . . . if that is possible.'

'Well,' she tried not to show her pleasure, 'it is my job, after all, to help women to look more beautiful than they really are, and ...' she shrugged, 'I guess that goes for myself, too.'

Looking back at the chalet, the tears she had shed during the night were forgotten and she decided to give herself up to the present. Laurent's chalet, she thought, seemed to respond to every change of mood and of light. At sunset the day before it had resembled a rare piece of flushed-pink jade on the green lawn. Now, however, it appeared dusky-pink in the hot sun and very islandish.

Some of the roads Laurent took to Curepipe were rutted and potholed. 'I am taking short cuts,' Laurent told her. 'I will link up with the main road presently. These potholes and ruts are from a bygone cyclone and have not been repaired. See that wash-away, over there?'

'Was the road washed away like that by a—*cyclone*?' Jade asked, astonished, widening her eyes.

'Does that make you nervous?' He turned to look at her, and laughed softly.

'Yes, it does. It makes me very nervous.'

Reaching for her hand, he said, 'Don't worry. We experience a very bad cyclone only every thirteen to fifteen years.'

'In what month?' Her eyes went to his tanned hand which covered her own.

'Oh ...' he shrugged and took his hand away, 'mostly January and February. Sometimes, in March.'

'It's February now,' she said.

'Yes. But don't let that worry you. We receive warning by radio well in advance.'

'Oh, and then?' She was conscious of suddenly being at ease with him.

'Well, we batten down, of course.' She had the feeling he was making light of it.

They were travelling inland. Some of the roads had been like passes, twisting up through the thick green growth of spice trees, strelitzia, palm and fern trees, and then often, for long spells at a time, they could not see anything over the tall sugar cane.

'What's that strange tall structure?' she asked, leaning towards him, and he turned to look at her quickly and their eyes met.

'It is a ruined sugar mill,' he said. 'You will like my house, I think.' He gave his attention to driving.

'What's it like?' she asked.

'Oh ...' she liked the way he always shrugged his shoulders in that French manner, 'poised ... hugging the slopes of a mountain ... snobbish, almost.'

'Snobbish?' She laughed. 'That's a strange way to describe a house.'

'It is a Mauritian house,' he explained. 'It is the sort of house a knowledgeable native builds to see him through cyclones.'

They were passing a bougainvillea-covered shack and she was prompted to say, 'A knowledgeable and wealthy native, don't you mean?'

'Yes, I'm afraid that is often the case here. Well then, it is a Mauritian house a knowledgeable and wealthy native builds to see him through cyclones ... and relatives coming from France.'

Jade laughed easily with him. While he had been talking she had been of the opinion that she had annoyed him with her remark.

'You are pleased you came now?' he asked, after a moment.

'Yes ... I don't really know, actually.'

'What do you mean—you don't really know?' His

mood seemed to change.

'I don't want to talk about it,' she said, 'but I shouldn't be gadding like this.'

'Translated, that means you are feeling guilty.' He turned to look at her, and when she made no reply he said, 'You have not answered my question.'

'Or course I feel guilty! Don't taunt me. Nicole de Spéville makes me feel even worse.'

'That is understandable, of course,' he shrugged. 'She would, but I suggest we put these two out of our minds today ... Nicole and Marlow Lewis. Right now,' he lifted her hand and brushed her fingers with his lips and she found herself thrilling to his touch, 'I am only aware of the fact that I have a very beautiful girl with me and I know the sensation of longing to please her.' Glancing at her, he said, 'Forget them.'

The way in which he referred to Nicole made it clear that, although he was involved with the beautiful Comtesse, he wished to ignore the fact at this particular time.

The sweet scent of sugar was in the Mauritian air. Jade tried to push her feelings of guilt to one side and to overlook the fact that Laurent Sevigny was not the sort to be faithful to any one girl. Neither did the clashing of ages appear to worry him.

'The mountains here always fascinate me,' he was saying against her fingers, 'heaved, as they were, into shape by volcanic eruptions so many, many ages ago.'

'They fascinate me too.' She turned to look moodily at him and then held her breath as he turned her hand over and kissed her palm.

'I'm going to take you somewhere first before we drive into Curepipe,' he said. 'It is called Trou aux Cerfs.'

When she tried to repeat it, after him, he laughed. 'Listen—Troo-oh-Serf. It is quite easy.'

'What is it?' she asked, swept up in his mood.

'Wait and see. It is a landmark.'

'Like your leaning palm?' she asked innocently and slanting her blue eyes at him.

'No, not like my leaning palm.' He turned to look at her. 'My leaning palm is a very private landmark, this is a tourist attraction.'

They were high up now and the town of Curepipe lay below them. When he had parked the car he said, 'Come. What you see now is an extinct volcanic crater. It means "hole of the deer".'

As they stood looking across the huge crater he came to stand very close to her and placing an arm about her he said, 'You spoke about the pyramids of rock in the cane fields. Here lies the explanation. Those fields are covered with basalt rocks and are heaped into mini-pyramids to enable the cane fields to be ploughed.'

'You can see half across the island from here,' said Jade, acutely aware of him. 'It's wonderful—and no tourists about at the moment.'

It was very breezy and the wind caught her dark hair and blew it across her face, and with his free hand Laurent smoothed it back. It was all a game with him, she knew, and yet she felt excited by him. 'Over there,' he turned her slightly and his hands were warm on her bare shoulders, 'you can see Trois Mamelles.'

'Troy-ma-mell,' she repeated after him, and laughed.

'That is right. You are coming on. There is supposed to be a similarity to bosoms.'

'Bosoms?' Suddenly she laughed. 'I don't think the description at all adequate. They look just what they are—ramparts.'

When he turned her round slowly to face him, her blue eyes searched his which were the colour of a moody sea. 'It depends on the owner,' he said and, bending his head, placed his lips on the small hollow which devided her breasts which were taut beneath the sun-frock.

'No, please, Laurent,' she protested.

'I prefer my women to be slender and stylish,' he told her. 'You, of course, answer to that description.'

As he straightened and took her into his arms she was thinking a little wildly that his skin was like un-flawed copper. She could feel the silky hairs on his chest, where his shirt was unbuttoned, against her own and again on his arms. It's just for today, she told herself consolingly. Just for today ... as much for him as for myself. ...

With rising excitement she responded to his kisses. She fought the thickening clouds of doubt which threatened to break up that excitement for her ... and won. Laurent's fingers were in her hair, on her throat. Dimly she was aware of the murmurings of Curepipe below and then of the sound of the purr of an engine as a car climbed the hill towards them.

'In any case,' said Laurent, releasing her, 'this is no place to make love. Here in Mauritius we have a saying and that is—it is no problem. There is plenty of time for us.'

Humiliated, she said, 'I think that's a stupid expression. Everybody has a problem from time to time. My problem right now is that I've allowed myself to be ... to be. ...'

'Yes?' His voice was curt.

'Well, caught up like this.' She gave him a kind of drowned look. Her eyes went to his chiselled mouth.

She felt fury rise in her against him. 'I wish you'd leave me alone!'

'Underlying your remark I detect constraint.' His green eyes held hers. Suddenly he reached out his hands and drew her head towards him, cupping it with his fingers which were in her hair. 'In other words, you are bothered by pretence. You don't want me to leave you alone.' He kissed her lightly on the lips and then released her. A short distance from them the car which they had heard had stopped and doors were being opened.

Curepipe was unlike any other town Jade had ever seen, with its bustling streets and pavements, trodden by people of many races ... people with chocolate-coloured faces, ebony faces, yellow faces, white faces.

Completely fascinated, her eyes took in the vivid saris of the Indian women, Creole girls still wearing the ever-popular mini, Chinese men in slacks and bright cotton shirts, Moslems in tarbooshes. Some people, she noticed, even appeared to be clad in rags.

Laurent parked the car and for a moment they sat watching the people go by, cramming the narrow basalt pavements. 'So,' he said, 'I suggest we enjoy ourselves.'

Jade bit her lip as he turned her face towards him, by placing his fingers beneath her chin. 'Enjoy Curepipe with me.' His eyes were serious. 'You know you want to. Am I right?'

'Yes.' She went on looking at him.

Taking his fingers from her face, he said, 'It is really quite modern, Curepipe, when you get used to it. Different, that is all. Here you will find shops stocked with Oriental and Western merchandise. Curepipe is good and it is bad ... like you.' He gave her a smile. 'And like you, Curepipe often weeps.'

'How do you know I weep?' she asked.

'I have you summed up,' he replied.

'And you think I'm bad?' There was an edge to her voice.

'If wanting—desiring—me to make love to you is bad, then yes, you are very bad.' His eyes went to her lips and then lifted to her own. There was a slight mocking expression in their green depths.

'You could say that a fault of yours,' she retorted, 'is that you're outrageously conceited. Like you, I'm just amusing myself.' As she said this, she knew a moment of despair. 'But tell me,' she tried to sound flippant, 'why does Curepipe weep? You didn't tell me.'

'It drizzles here, quite often,' he told her. She knew that he was annoyed with her and it gave her satisfaction. 'However, it clears just as quickly. You see, it is nearly six hundred metres above sea level. During the winter nights it is common for people here to light a fire.' Suddenly he leaned over her side and undid the door-catch for her and then he was at her side, as she stepped on to the teeming pavement.

He had parked outside a large oriental-looking shop and, taking her arm, he guided her towards the entrance.

'This is my other interest on the island,' he told her.

'Apart from women, you mean?' a devil prompted her to say.

'Yes, apart from women,' his voice was almost brutal, she found herself thinking, 'and apart from my interest in the hotel and sister hotels, this is my other interest. I have already mentioned to you that collecting fine things is in my blood—in the blood of my family—and for this reason, I decided to open this shop in Curepipe. My family are interested in such goings-on in France. I wanted to surprise you with the beauty confined in this shop, but you are doing your best to destroy this surprise with your childish remarks. I think this is the most sought-after shop in Mauritius—it *is* the most sought-after shop, no two ways about it. The tourist with money comes here. I, of course, have a staff here and the entire project is managed for me by a person I hold in high esteem. In a shop such as this, prices are fixed. In small, obscure shops, however, the prices demanded are often far above the value of the goods ... so beware of this when you shop. But in any case, you are expected to haggle. The shopkeeper expects it.'

'It seems awful to have to haggle,' she said, as they entered the cool, quiet shop.

'Not at all. It is an act of trade and certainly not undignified, here in Mauritius.'

There was an immediate rustle of tension on the part of the staff as Laurent Sevigny entered the shop. Jade watched him as he spoke to the people who served behind wide glass counters and glass shelves. He spoke to them in French. Glancing around, she saw that there were shelves of thick glass right round the walls and these shelves were filled with jade, ivory, precious stones, carvings, jewellery, porcelain, brass, bronze, wood and ceramics.

'So?' He came to stand beside her. 'What do you think?'

'Oh,' she let out a long breath, 'it's just too beautiful! I don't know where to look first. It's—it's like a treasure house!'

'It is a treasure house. Many of these treasures speak of a bygone age. They have involved extensive travel on my part.'

'I had no idea that such beautiful things were in here, as we sat in the car outside,' she commented.

'Many of these works of art were wrought by masters.' She watched him pick up a hand-carved wooden Chinese *gyojya* priest, delicately tooled and holding a sacred scroll. Eyes of polished glass glittered back at them. 'This, for instance.' As her eyes rested on those tanned, well-shaped fingers, she found herself thinking that it was right and fitting that they should hold the exquisite carving.

'It—it must have cost the earth,' she said, feeling again the sensation of those fingers in her hair, her face, her throat. . . .

'It did—and does.' He placed it back on the glass shelf.

'Do you ever make mistakes?' she asked. 'That is, have you ever bought something only to discover that it's not what you believed it to be?'

'No.' His green eyes went over her. 'I never make mistakes, and I always know what I want and why I want it.' There was, she noticed, a kind of anger in the reply.

'Where is the white jade phoenix you told me about?' she asked.

'That is not for sale. It is at my house. Here instead is a white dragon.'

Placing her fingers on it, she said, 'It's perfect. Your shop is rather like a—temple of civilisation, don't you think?' She looked at him and bit her lip.

'Yes, it is, and with you at this moment its high priestess. But no, that is not how I look at it. The treasures you see here are to be enjoyed, not worshipped.'

'Like the high priestess in question, merely ... enjoyed.'

'I am not exactly priestess minded,' he told her. 'This here is a twelfth century Chinese stone Buddha....'

For a while they walked round the shop and then he said, 'I am taking you to lunch at a restaurant called La Potinière, rated by many as the best eating place on the island. There are rooms where one can wash and freshen up. I suggest a change of mood on your part, in order that you might enjoy the cuisine, which is superb French. A speciality is *sauce rouge de camarons et palmistes*. While we are in the process of this meal I do not wish to discuss either Marlow Lewis or Nicole de Spéville and, while I am with you, I certainly do not wish to be reminded of other women.'

'Marlow exists, nevertheless,' she retorted.

'He exists, yes, but it is a logical conclusion that in the end you will choose somebody nearer your own age.'

'And yet you yourself don't practise this advice.' She gave him a level look.

At that moment a girl came down the staircase, which was to one side of the shop and which obviously served the offices which must be on another floor. She had a pale, ivory skin and tawny eyes. She was wearing a vivid green shirt which was tucked into black slacks and she was breathtakingly beautiful. For a moment the tawny eyes did not seem to focus properly, and then surprise and excitement crossed her face.

'Laurent!' Coming quickly towards him she said, 'But I did not know this. For how long, Laurent? How long have you been back?'

Everything seemed to spin as Jade watched the girl as she went into Laurent's arms. 'I didn't know,' the girl kept murmuring as she moved her lips beneath his. As she moved her head from side to side her dark hair swirled silkily about her shoulders. 'But I don't understand,' she said, when the kiss had ended. The tawny eyes went towards Jade. 'You—you didn't bring a—bride back with you?' The ivory face paled visibly.

'No, you are fanciful. This is Jade Lawford from Australia. She is new to the island.' Looking at Jade, Laurent went on, 'I want you to meet Marcelle Fabré. She very efficiently manages this business for me.'

'I've come here to be married,' Jade explained, to show Laurent that the meeting with Marcelle Fabré was of little consequence so far as she was concerned. 'You might know him—Marlow Lewis.'

'Marlow Lewis!' Marcelle Fabré looked surprised. 'Yes—but only slightly. Where are you staying?'

'I'm staying at the Hotel Chalian and working there, as a matter of fact. I'm a beautician at the health clinic.'

'So ...?' The tawny eyes went over Jade. 'You work for the Comtesse de Spéville, in other words?' Glancing at Laurent she went on, 'You have brought Miss Lawford to shop, maybe?'

'I wanted to show her around,' he replied. 'I especially wished her to see some of our rare jade pieces.'

There was an awkward moment, then he said, 'But right now we are going to have lunch.'

'And you, of course, are at your chalet?' Marcelle's tawny eyes did not leave his face.

'Yes. What do you want me to say ... that I am at the other end of the island?' Laughing softly, he lifted a strand of her hair. When Marcelle replied in French Jade turned away and began looking at the beautiful items on the heavy glass shelving. Beyond the glass windows the arcade in which Laurent Sevigny's shop was situated was a lively kaleidoscope of people jostling one another.

A party of American tourists entered the shop which, she thought, must surely be the most exciting shop of its kind in Mauritius. People who bought here would have to be millionaires. As they attended to the Americans the staff were unruffled and polite. A faint smell of incense permeated the shop.

Laurent and the girl continued to talk in low voices, then he left her and came across to where Jade was standing.

'Are you ready for lunch?' He sounded annoyed. His mood had changed.

'Yes,' she replied. 'If we *have* to eat lunch.'

'What kind of nonsensical talk is that? It was our intention to eat lunch, was it not?'

'I believe so, yes, but I thought things might have changed for you.' Her mind was moving ahead to the things she planned to say to him in the near future.

'I am beginning to lose patience with you,' he snapped. 'Come along.'

Lifting one slim shoulder, her fingers continued tracing the eyes of a bronze Foo dog on an emerald and pearl pedestal and she did not look at him.

She caught her breath and then glared at him as he caught her hand.

'You make having lunch with you sound like an order,' she said.

'It is an order.' His fingers were firm on her arm as he guided her from the shop. 'It is not far,' he went on. 'We will walk.'

While they walked her eyes scanned the shops, which all appeared to stock wide ranges of Oriental and Western merchandise and a great variety of traditional craft products, including wood carvings, articles made of tortoiseshell, seashells, horn, leather and basket-work. There was also Indian jewellery and Mauritian pottery and Chinese embroideries, silks, ivory and jade contrasted with rolls of vivid materials. Many of the shops had fascinating names such as City of Peking and all appeared to offer a wide range of goods from China, Hong Kong, Japan, Thailand, the Philippines, Indonesia and Mauritius, judging by some of the price-tags. It was all very colourful and exciting and the man walking beside her was exciting—but something had gone out of the day. She felt suddenly depressed and bad-tempered.

A heavy, church-like door, adorned with huge hinges, led to the powder-room in the restaurant, and here, Jade tried to soothe her ruffled feelings by washing her face and hands and applying fresh make-up.

They ate an excellent lunch and, although she felt peeved and let-down, Jade discovered that she was hungry.

'What are you thinking about?' Laurent asked.

'Nothing,' she replied.

'What *is* it with you?' he snapped. 'Nothing. Who thinks of—nothing?' His eyes went over her face.

'If you must know,' she said, 'I was thinking that the restaurant comes as a surprise, after everything I've seen.'

'You mean, of course, with its vast fireplace and many pieces of gleaming copper? This would remind you of England, naturally.'

'Yes.' She was suddenly sad. 'The crockery is staid white and bordered in royal blue with that band of gold.' She traced a finger round the thin line of gold on her bread-plate. 'It's very British, in a way, especially with the royal blue tablecloth and smaller ones in white over it.'

'It is a French restaurant,' he told her, 'but nevertheless you feel at home here, no?'

'Talking about home, you're a long way from home,' she said.

'I go and come as I please,' he told her. 'I have made this island my home now.'

'You have a cold streak in you.' Her eyes glittered. 'Don't you miss your family?'

There was an unmistakable shade of impatience in his voice when he answered. 'I can see my family whenever I wish. I am an islander, but still belong to the jet-set.'

'And of course, you're not nervous in one ... an airliner, I mean. You've proved that, just as you've proved a whole lot of other things.' Her voice was tight.

'Oh?' He drew the word out, and sat back and looked at her. 'Such as?'

Jade checked her temper, which was rising again. 'Oh, forget it. What difference does it make, anyway? Do you know,' she went on with a rush, 'it's just struck me—I didn't see one supermarket in Curepipe, as we walked here.'

'*Supermarket!*' He looked back at her with angry astonishment. 'But we were not discussing supermarkets. You were talking about me, as a matter of fact.'

'I suddenly thought better of it,' she shrugged.

'I didn't like what you said about me.' His dark, sea-green eyes were cold.

'I'm not asking you to like it, am I?'

'I think what it amounts to is that you are not sure about me. Right?' He went on looking at her.

'It's really of little importance.'

'No? I think it is very important,' he said.

'You really do remind me of a corsair,' she told him. 'I've read of the dazzling career of one of them. I can't think of his name, but anyway, he seized booty worth millions of francs. To the islanders he was a dashing hero. He eventually owned property all over the island and had a fortune in France. Does this ring a bell with you? And I suppose he owned women, too.'

'No doubt he did, and no doubt he commanded good service. Are you quite through?' he asked.

'No, I'm not quite through. I just want you to know that I have no intention of being *one* of your women!' Her voice had risen now and she glanced quickly in the direction of nearby tables and bar of almost black wood, to one side of them.

'You are jealous,' he said, speaking with a deliberate, brutal carelessness.

'What a stupid thing to say! I'm not jealous!'

'Hah! Beware of the girl who says she is not jealous.' He gave her a scornful glance and began eating again and, as she looked at him, Jade was aware of an arrogance in him, which stemmed from the knowledge that she was attracted to him.

'I don't know how I got into this,' she said, looking across the table at him, with hostile, angry eyes.

Lifting his lashes, he gave her another scornful look. 'Because you are jealous, that is why.'

Finally it was time to reach for her bag and they went back to where Laurent's car was parked. She was surprised when he did not suggest going back into the shop again.

'You are fortunate,' he said, turning to look at her

as if nothing out of the ordinary had happened between them.

'Really? Why is that?' Her blue eyes were still hostile.

'Curepipe is often veiled by cloud and drizzle.'

Already they were seeing sugar-cane which she knew by now grew right down almost to the breeze-caressed beaches. In places, the road was littered with sticks of cane, which had dropped from the trucks carrying them from the fields to the mills.

'All Mauritius lives for sugar—and by it,' Laurent went on, 'in other words that means it supplies the daily bread. The industry is one of the oldest in the world, dating back nearly . . .' moodily she watched him lift his shoulders, 'three and a half centuries.' Suddenly he reduced speed to crawl behind a cart drawn by a hump-backed zeba beast. 'These are the cattle of Mauritius,' he told her. When she made no reply he turned to look at her.

'I am beginning to lose patience by your silence.'

'I'm feeling—upset,' she told him, moving more to her side of the car.

'So you are feeling upset. Perhaps this is because Marlow Lewis is away in South Africa when he should be here with you? But somehow I don't think so. I will point out the beginning of Marlow's plantation for you, very shortly. You will not be able to see the house—only the entrance and road to it, through the cane fields.'

'I didn't know we'd passed it on our way to Curepipe,' she said, feeling panic, laced with curiosity. 'You didn't mention it.'

'For the very simple reason that this is a different route now.'

When he turned off the road on to what apparently was the beginning of a private road she glanced quickly at him. 'This is it.' He turned to look at her.

On either side of the road, and where the tall sugar cane ended, there was a vivid profusion of red and pink hibiscus. Laurent slowed down and stopped the car. 'You would like to see the house now? I can drive up there. Or do you prefer this with your future husband?'

'Now,' she said, after a moment, and touched her lips with her tongue. Her mouth felt suddenly dry. 'Now, if you think it will be all right?'

'Whether it will be all right or not has nothing to do with me,' he said shortly, 'but in any case, we will go.'

Marlow's house was like the location of a period film, Jade found herself thinking as she saw it, with its pillared verandahs overlooking the lawns and, in turn, all that sugar cane. In the distance they could see the ocean and, in the silence, could hear dogs barking.

Laurent had parked the car immediately in front of the wide steps which led up to the verandah, and almost immediately Jade's eyes had gone to the horns on the wall, which served to remind her that Marlow was now a hunter. A little shiver ran down her spine.

'Get out, if you wish.' Laurent's voice conveyed nothing. 'There should be servants about.'

He came to stand next to her and she made a pretence of admiring the hibiscus, bougainvillea, oleander and poinsettia shrubs.

'He must keep dogs.' Her voice was small.

'He *does* keep dogs,' he replied very softly.

'You know how to hurt me and you like to hurt me, don't you?' she said bitterly.

'I don't own those dogs,' he said angrily, 'because

you know without being told that they are hunting dogs, no?'

'And that's how they hunt here?' she said dully.

'Yes. The hunters take up position on wooden observation platforms. . . .'

'I saw them—and wondered,' she cut in, still in that same lifeless voice.

'These are known as *miradors chut*, hidden below by foliage. They simply wait. The deer are driven towards them by dogs or beaters. Two does, I think it is, and one stag. That is the ration, and, as I have already explained to you, the day ends on a boisterous and successful note . . . champagne, ice-cold island rum, soda-filled whiskies, whisky on the rocks. . . .'

'Stop it! *Stop it!*' she repeated.

When he caught her and swung her round to face him he said, 'This is the man you are going to marry, you little fool! The dogs there in the pens among the bananas, paw-paw trees, litchi and mango trees belong to him. So do the box-like trailers with iron guards on the sides belong to him. You will have to see them every day when you are here. Think about that! This is the man who gives you twenty years, that you have come here to marry.'

When he bent his head to kiss her she closed her eyes. His kisses would enable her to bear the intolerable weight of the burden that was pressing down on her, she thought.

'Don't take it out on me,' he muttered, his lips going from her mouth to her eyelids, her throat.

As her lips parted under his she knew that she had been manipulated again.

'After you are married, you can dismiss me from your mind,' Laurent said.

'Yes,' she murmured, clinging to him. 'Yes. . . .'

If you can, she was thinking, in the shattering, hopeless flood of desire she was feeling for him, but right now, she didn't care.

When the elderly Creole woman coughed on the verandah, they broke apart.

'We are not—coming in,' Laurent said.

'He is away,' the woman told him.

'Yes, I know,' he replied, and then to Jade, 'We will go now you have seen it.' She allowed him to take her hand.

When they were in the car he said, 'We will go back to my chalet and drink island cocktails among the leaning palms and a pink sunset.'

For a moment his sea-green eyes were on her mouth, and then he reached for her again and his lips sought hers.

'The woman. . . .' she murmured.

'For sure,' he said, and smiled suddenly. 'I can wait.'

For several moments, they studied each other, then he started the car.

CHAPTER FIVE

'You see,' he said, 'there is a pink sunset.' He took her hand, and raising it, kissed her fingers. When he released it again he touched the nape of her neck, and Jade tried to think of an ivory-skinned girl with tawny eyes.

'It's been nearly an all-day affair,' she murmured, 'going up to Curepipe.'

'Come,' he said, 'and while you sit on the balcony I

will mix you a drink, then we will admire the coral-reef and the sunset before I take you back to the hotel.'

The sea was a mixture of turquoise, changing to amber which finally began to look as if it had been dusted with pearl. The thin, foaming line beyond the sea lagoon was surprisingly quiet and calm, and yet, Marlow had written, there were places where the wild Indian Ocean pounded, unchecked, against black, cane-bordered sea cliffs.

'Service is swift and polite,' said Laurent, when he passed Jade a drink.

'So I see. Thank you.' Taking the glass from him she watched as he chose one of the cane chairs. 'It's perfect here.' Her eyes went to the fishermen who were busy working on their boats under the palms. 'What do you call that funny thing on the water?'

'It is a catamaran,' he told her. 'It is time I threw a gala.' He seemed preoccupied, but she knew he was joking. 'But no, now is not the time. I have a need for complete privacy. Marlow Lewis, I understand, often gives a party. I have been to only two, and that was because Nicole asked me to take her there.'

She knew that he was waiting for her reaction.

'Oh?' She felt tense. 'What kind of parties does he give? If he gives parties I expect a lot will rest on me, in the not-too-distant future. But in any case, you did mention that you didn't want to talk about Marlow?'

'A little wild. . . .' he ignored her last remark.

For a moment she was quiet, looking down at her glass, then she said, 'He didn't used to give wild parties in Australia.'

'No?' He glanced at her, as if not believing her.

'No. He and Elisa lived in the main house. They—they weren't married, but they were going to be married. Jeffrey, my brother, and I were in the small bungalow. Jeffrey helped manage the sheep-station. We'd met Marlow in London. Jeffrey had always longed to farm and when Marlow made the offer he went to Australia, taking me with him.'

'Of course,' Laurent held up his glass and gazed through the golden liquid, 'the plantation house without its virile owner appeared switched off today, but once you are married and living there it will take on a different meaning. The dogs, of course, you will have to accept. It is part of his life. If you marry him it will be a part of yours.'

'I didn't know he was interested in hunting.' Jade saw that her hand was shaking when she lifted the glass. 'I didn't know him all that well, though.'

'You must have known him well enough—otherwise you would not be here,' he answered shortly.

The Indian Ocean sunset was painting the white beach a rich pink now, and dramatised the palms.

'That is so, no?' His voice sounded suddenly harsh.

Glancing at his face to see how the remark was meant, she explained, 'After the plane crash, we were thrown together. We—sort of—consoled one another.'

'You moved into his house with him?'

'No!' she replied furiously. 'I did not move into his house with him. How dare you say that to me?'

'It is a matter of indifference to me,' he said brutally, 'whether or not you moved in with him.' He got up, suddenly, and went into the adjoining studio. Jade could hear him pouring liquid into a glass.

'What about London? Your people?' he asked, coming out to the balcony again.

'There were no people. Our people were ... honestly,' she put her glass down and covered her face with her fingers, 'it's all too much ... you see, they were killed....'

'Don't go on,' he said. 'I'm sorry—forgive me.'

'After the air crash,' she took her fingers away, 'Jeffrey's, I mean, not my parents', I moved to Sydney. I went back to salon work and Marlow and I corresponded. Finally he wrote asking me to join him here.'

'After how long?' He seemed impatient for her reply.

'Soon after he got here.'

'Letters giving way to *love*-letters strengthened the relationship, no? But he has been here for some time now ... two years, I understand. Why did it take you so long to come to him?'

'He wrote saying....' she began, but he cut her short.

'He had his reasons, that is obvious. Marlow Lewis....' he gazed out at the water. 'The great hunter.' His voice was sarcastic.

'You are, in your own way, a hunter,' she said hotly. 'The only difference is that you happen to be a woman-hunter!'

'My life is like an obstacle race, but then I am excited by obstacles,' he replied. 'I am like an athlete, not a hunter.'

Suddenly she stood up.

'Does this upset you?' he was saying.

'No, it doesn't. I just don't want to stay here sparring with you. My nerves are on edge, right now. Everything seems to have gone wrong. I don't feel like going back to my room and yet I most certainly do not feel like staying here. I can hardly believe that I work at the health clinic. How long ago is it since I worked there? Only yesterday? Already,' she went on bitterly, 'it seems a lifetime ago. I wish I was back in my flat in Chelsea.'

'You are upset.' He came to stand next to her.

'And you have seen to it.'

'Look,' he said, placing his arms about her, 'here in Mauritius we have a saying which is—tomorrow belongs to no one. Let us forget about yesterday—and tomorrow. We will dine together this evening, at the hotel. I know what I want and you know what you want—but for this evening, let us put these things aside.'

'I feel so tired,' she murmured, against him. 'Tired of everything.'

'You don't,' he smoothed back her hair. 'You feel excited by everything. For myself, I have no nostalgia for the yesterdays ... so far as women are concerned. I have no plans for the future. Now is what counts—let us enjoy it while it lasts.'

He had dinner with her at the hotel. Nicole de Spéville was also dining there, with a small party of friends, and when she saw Jade and Laurent she commented, 'You have been getting around, Jade. Marlow must appear to you as a dream, almost, no? After all, you have not seen him for two years, and he was unable to be here on your arrival to remind you that he really does exist.'

'Well, the fact that he's not here, Nicole, is hardly my fault ... and yes, it all does seem like a dream.'

After Nicole had passed by, Jade sat looking down at the honey-gold tablecloth. As usual, there was a spray of pink and red hibiscus arranged on the cloth ... just clustered there, without water—without a vase. Soon, Jade thought, they would wilt and die, but like the women in Laurent Sevigny's life, there were more in the garden, just waiting to be picked.

'Nicole was young to be left a widow,' Laurent broke into her thoughts.

'Her attitude towards me has something to do with you.' Jade gave him a level look.

'Allow me to remind you that her attitude towards you has nothing to do with me.'

'I find that difficult to believe,' she said.

'Let me remind you, anyhow, that it happens to be the case. We are merely good friends,' he replied.

'It depends on what you mean by good friends. You are the essence of elusiveness.' While she was speaking she sensed his hostility.

'It is not for *me* to explain Nicole.'

After dinner they watched the Sega dancing, but Laurent did not ask her to dance.

When he finally saw her to her door he said, 'I do not have to explain Marlow Lewis to you either. You are the one who is going to have to face up to him. Sometimes you try my patience, and my advice to you is do not push me to the limit, because I might just tell you more than you'd care to hear about this man.'

In the morning, Jade went to her world of beauty. Beauty which meant discipline, from dawn to dusk, a putting on of one's best face, or getting someone else to put it on for you, glorious bouncy hair, a good figure ... and finally, the reason for wanting to be lovely ... a man in the background.

In the reception office Nicole was already there, wearing one of her caftans. 'After all,' she was saying, 'what does one do when one is overweight and depressed? Go on looking and feeling terrible? No, I think not. No, darling, you were quite right in coming here to Mauritius to the health clinic. Why feel guilty, for goodness' sake? After all, your husband could have come with you, no? He was just acting like a mule. Why have a guilt complex over this, but quite possibly your three-day liquid diet is having something to do with it. Have you been drinking your anti-morbs? Ah, Jade—excuse me, darling.' Nicole moved away from the woman she had been talking to. 'Jade, I want you to look at these latest photographs of that big pain in the neck. Cellulite. Doesn't it look like orange-rind when squeezed? Look at those legs! By the way, when Marian has finished her anti-cellulite heat-treatment, she is to have a facial.'

There was nothing but politeness in Nicole's manner. I could have liked her, Jade found herself thinking, if it hadn't been for Laurent Sevigny. She promised herself a drink of the magical anti-morbs health drink, for she certainly had a fit of the blues and the anti-depressant drink might be as beneficial to her as it was to someone on a liquid or very strict diet.

Jade went through to the machine department where clients had decorated the walls with praise. This, in fact, formed part of the decor. One of the longest read:

So I went away for two months and a day,
To Mauritius in the sea,
To a protein diet and saunas and quiet,
And look what's happened to me!
The Comtesse Nicole machine-vibrated my spleen,
My buttocks, my thighs—and my bo',
And when summer came
They measured my frame
And told me I could go.
I love you all—so much.
Thank you!

It was a world of hydrotherapy, parafango, cellulite heat machines, Propil, electrotherapy and ionto-phoreses, and it was Greek to most people, but it coped with water massage, therapeutic volcanic mud treatment for fibrositis, hair removal, slimming, crêpy necks and wrinkled faces.

The salon was restful and subdued, with its soft lighting and rose-tinted mirrors, and while she worked on people's faces, Jade thought about Marlow Lewis, the man she had come to marry, and of Laurent Sevigny, the man with whom she had fallen hopelessly in love.

She did not see or hear of him for two days, and then she met him in the boutique. Wondering what he was doing in a place with white urns and dried and treated skeletal white leaves, white lace-like flowers, hand-painted caftans, Oriental kimonos, bamboo stools and small ornaments, she said uncertainly, 'Oh, hello.'

'I was looking for you,' he said, his eyes going over her.

'Oh?' She felt her heart lurch.

'Only today I discovered your sun-glasses in my car.'

'Where are they?' she asked, seeing that he was empty-handed.

'At my chalet, waiting to be collected by their owner.' Suddenly he smiled. 'Did you think I would return them? What have you been doing with yourself?'

The brooding, troubled words of a song sounded softly in the boutique, for music was piped just about everywhere in the hotel and in the health hydro.

'Oh, working,' Jade said, 'but I'm enjoying it. In its way, it's very rewarding work. The boost on beauty is enormous on women and, apart from that, there's the health side to it.'

'Are you finished here?' He glanced around the boutique.

'Yes,' she said.

'Well,' he took her arm and walked with her to the door, 'men would tell you that the very best thing for skin and beauty is making love.'

In the cool, vaulted arcade she moved away from his touch. When she spoke her voice was cool. 'The idea of therapeutic sex doesn't appeal to me, I'm afraid.'

'And I sincerely hope you don't have to resort to it,' he mocked her. 'Your sunglasses are waiting for you to call for them.'

After he had gone Jade stood biting her lip. While he had said this his sea-green eyes had been fixed on her in demanding scrutiny and they had insisted that she look at him. It amused him, she found herself thinking bitterly, to get her to do things she didn't want to do, for she wanted to go back to his chalet. He knew that.

When her telephone rang that evening she felt like collapsing at the sound of Marlow's voice.

'I'm speaking to you from Reunion,' he told her. 'The island. How are you, Jade?'

'I-I'm fine.'

'I'm sorry it had to be like this,' he was saying, 'but it couldn't be helped.'

'That's all right,' she assured him, but she was thinking that he might have phoned her before this or, at least left a letter for her to have read on her arrival in Mauritius.

There was a pause and then he said, 'And so you are quite settled in with—with Nicole, then?'

'Yes.'

'And the work?' he asked.

'Yes. It's what I've been used to, of course. It's what I was trained to be—a beauty therapist. The clinic is full, with a good smattering of men. I thought you were in South Africa?'

'I was. I've touched down in Reunion. I have some matters to attend to here.'

'I drove out to your house,' she told him, and waited.

'Oh?' His voice sounded strained. 'And what did you think of it?'

'I didn't go in, of course, but it's a gracious old house—everything you said it was.'

'Look, Jade, I'm sorry to have to tell you I won't be back for another few days,' he said. 'Go out to the house, if you wish. Maybe you have things you want to take there?'

'My belongings—the things I wanted to bring with me—will be arriving later,' she told him, 'but in any case, thank you.'

After the call she walked about aimlessly, going from her room to the balcony and back. Her mind felt as if it was staggering beneath a weight of pressure and bewilderment.

She longed to be able to approach Nicole about the uncertainty she was experiencing, but realised that she could not do this. After all, it was her own fault, for she had done nothing about the inevitable, which was seeing too much of Laurent Sevigny and falling in love with him.

If she'd been a man, right now, she was thinking wildly, she would go and sit on one of the stools at the cocktail bar and get hopelessly and traditionally drunk. As it was, being a woman, she could only suffer.

Her pride would not allow her to go to the chalet for the sunglasses. Once she picked up her phone with the intention of phoning Laurent to tell him that she was coming, but quickly changed her mind.

Apart from the health clinic, Nicole de Spéville also ran a training school where students studied all branches of beauty culture, with individual and personal attention by Nicole herself. There were at the moment three students and during weekends they 'worked' on clients, thus gaining valuable practical experience in client/operator relationship, under actual salon conditions. This left Jade comparatively free to do as she pleased.

It was for this reason that she decided to get away from everything, and the obvious place to go seemed to be her future home. After all, there were servants there, and Marlow had suggested that she might like to go there.

On the Friday afternoon, when she had finished at the salon, she drove to Marlow's house in the mini-bus, after arranging with the Creole driver to drop her off there and pick her up again on the Monday morning.

The wind started to blow in full force just after midday and she almost cancelled the lift in the mini-bus. From her balcony she saw that several fishing vessels had come in and if she had not already phoned Marlow's Creole housekeeper, explaining her intention to spend the weekend there, she would have cancelled her plans. Although the idea of going to a strange house filled her with unease and depression she allowed herself to drift on the tide and let herself in for yet another form of the kind of punishment she seemed intent on inflicting upon herself.

She was the last passenger to alight from the mini-bus and Philipee, the driver, said, 'I wonder what the met office at Vacoas will have to say about the weather?'

'Oh, so there is a met office on the island?' She tried to overcome the unease she was now feeling, and glanced towards the steps of Marlow's house.

'Yes, it supplies the weather forecast for shipping and flying and it warns the islanders in the cyclone season, when these winds get up,' Philipee told her.

'But you don't think there's going to be a cyclone, do you?' Her blue eyes were frightened.

Laughing easily, he said, 'No, I don't think so. I didn't mean to frighten you. Have you heard of Paul and Virginie yet?'

She was puzzled. 'No. Who are they?'

'During the night in August, 1744, a ship was wrecked. All through our history ships have been wrecked in cyclones. This was the *St Géran*, and a hundred and fifty people were drowned and all cargo lost. Only nine people escaped, and we have this story of Paul and Virginie. They are something like your Romeo and Juliet. They were lovers. He saw Virginie drown and he was so brokenhearted that he fled into the forest where he died of a broken heart. When Virginie's body was washed up the two lovers were buried together. There's a statue of Paul and Virginie in the Curepipe town gardens.'

The story depressed her and she said, 'Do you think I should come back with you to the hotel, Philipee?'

Suddenly he laughed. 'There won't be a cyclone, miss. Don't be frightened.'

'But,' Jade turned to look at Marlow's plantation-house, 'it's only a *wooden* house.'

'Yes, but look how long it's been standing. This is a Victorian house, miss.'

She stood watching him as he turned the bus round and drove off and was hidden from sight by the tall cane.

What was it Nicole had said about Marlow's house? Gracious, colonial ... built of tropical wood—under the constant threat of cyclones....

There was an old-fashioned knocker and she used it, and while she waited she stood looking at the wind, which could only be described as violent, she thought. Just when she was beginning to despair that the house was unoccupied, the door opened and she was almost dragged inside by an elderly Creole woman who said, 'Quickly, miss. Everything bangs, if a door is opened. My name is Marie and I am Monsieur Marlow's house-keeper. I stay here on the property with my husband and daughter Juanita. We didn't think you would come, but we prepared for you, anyway. The weather is getting worse, every minute. Come, I show you your room.'

Except for the buffeting of the wind which caused it to shudder, the house was very quiet. The room to which Jade was shown was furnished with the mini-mum of casual furnishings and there were shutters at the windows, which had been closed. Because of the gloomy conditions this brought about, Marie switched on the light.

'It's—it's a typical sugar-plantation house, isn't it?' Jade commented, feeling ill at ease. 'Even to the fan whirring from the high ceiling.'

'So you have been in a plantation house before?' Marie sounded curious.

'No,' Jade laughed, 'but,' she shrugged, 'you know how a person pictures something in their mind.'

The walls, she noticed, were painted an almost

bright blue and the window frames were white. Twin beds were separated by a bamboo table and the floor was uncarpeted, but rush matting divided the space between the beds. There was red hibiscus, freshly cut, arranged carelessly in a blue-and-white vase.

'Monsieur Marlow's bedroom is just across the passage,' said Marie. 'You would like to see it?'

A feeling of sheer despair washed over Jade. 'No. No, thank you . . . not now.'

'Please to make yourself at home. Soon, of course, you will be married and this will be your home,' Marie went on, while something in Jade screamed, no, no, no. . .!

However, it was a pleasant enough house. The sitting-room, as Marie referred to it, was detailed in straw and bamboo and tall potted palms grew in woven baskets, bound in leather. A fan made whirring noises over the wind noises. It was close and hot. Highbacked cane chairs brought glamour into the room.

The wind continued to batter the plantation house, which seemed to be very much at the mercy of it. Now that she was actually here, Jade asked herself what it was she had planned to do. She had had visions of herself washing flimsy drapes and of hanging them out on the washline to float about in the wind, after which she would hang them and stand back to gaze at them, and admire them. But there were no flimsy drapes at the windows of this house. There was about it a tropical-island environment with its louvred hurricane shutters, bamboo shades and pristine wicker furniture and rush-matting.

Later, Marie came to the door. 'I have prepared dinner for you. Monsieur Marlow has what he calls his sundowner first, sometimes two, sometimes three,' she smiled. 'If you would like this I will show you where to find it and fetch ice for you.'

The house shook and Jade felt her first strong twist of fear. 'Thank you—something is very much wrong with the weather, isn't it? Don't you think we'd better phone the met office to find out?'

'The phone is out of order, but we have had warning one, miss, on the radio. I did not tell you. I didn't want to worry you.'

Moistening her lips, which felt suddenly dry, Jade queried, 'Warning *one*?'

'Yes. Warning one means that a cyclone is somewhere in the area.'

'Oh, no! What do we do?'

'Nothing. We wait for warning two. If we get another signal we must prepare to take shelter.'

'But where? Is there some kind of—shelter—you know, like an air-raid shelter?'

'There are cyclone shelters, yes, but not here. We keep indoors, fasten everything down,' Marie told her.

'You seem so calm,' Jade said, feeling ashamed of the fear she was feeling.

'Well,' Marie lifted her palms, 'you can't run from it. You sit it out. But who knows, it might pass us. Come, I show you something.'

Leading Jade into what was no doubt Marlow's study, she said, 'This is a track chart.'

Jade saw that the caption read: Cyclones in the Indian Ocean. The chart did not make sense, of course, but she was able to gather that Mauritius was in the cyclone belt and that the cyclone season was December to April, with January and February the peak period.

'See the names,' Marie began to read aloud, 'Ginette, Joelle, Claudine, Dominique, Yvonne, Carmen, Janet ... see, all girls' names.'

Some of the names had INTENSE written beneath them.

The drink which Jade poured for herself did nothing to curb the apprehension she was feeling. While she was sipping it, the first squall hit the house, ripping its way through the harbour of Port Louis and the fantastically shaped mountains and the cyclone was on its way.

'It's coming,' said Marie. 'When the big winds come, they will shake the island.' She carried a portable radio and stood in the doorway to the sitting-room. 'We have had warning two, miss. Don't open anything, no doors, no windows, nothing.'

'What about the dogs?' Jade asked.

'Oh, the dogs have shelter ... made of cast-iron,' Marie replied.

Above the noise of the wind and rain, they heard the knocker and Marie said, 'Somebody in trouble. I get Louis, my husband, to go.'

When the door to the wide hall was opened they could feel the suction it caused all over the house, and then the door banged.

'It could take all the windows,' Louis's voice was loud. 'This way, please.'

When Laurent Sevigny came into the room his eyes went straight to Jade. 'Why the devil did you not leave word? Philipee, the driver, told me eventually.' While a huge feeling of relief washed over her he went on, 'I am taking you to my house. There is no time to make it back to the hotel.' Turning to the Creole couple he said, 'This is her first experience of this nature.'

It took them all their time to get to the car and it seemed like madness to be leaving the house. The shrubs and trees bent and shrank to avoid the tantrum of the gale force wind and everywhere cane seemed to be heaving and swaying.

Jade clung to Laurent's arm, loving him in all the confusion. Even from the steps leading down from the verandah the car was hardly visible.

It was only after Laurent had helped her into the car that she was able to sort herself out and she discovered that she was in the back seat. Marcelle Fabré, the girl who managed his shop, was in the front seat and her long black hair was wet and she was shivering. She completely ignored Jade.

The road up to the plantation-house which had been rutted and potholed before, as a result of some other tropical storm, seemed to be practically washed away now and it was obvious that Laurent was having difficulty in getting the car through, quite apart from holding it steady. Because of the lashing rain, visibility was practically nil. It was plain that the mood of sea and land were matched now, as water surged in, lashed and swept along by the wind.

Rain and wind attacked the car so that it seemed to be lifting and wide-eyed and frightened the two girls peered through the eerie light. The whole sensation was one of bending, gyrating cane and trees. It was a raging wilderness, whipped by the howling gale and lashing rain ... another world, in fact, thought Jade, her teeth chattering. The sea which controlled the weather on the island had gone insane.

CHAPTER SIX

'Thank God for electricity,' said Laurent. 'Apparently the lines can't be down.'

Jade and Marcelle stood watching him as he switched on lamps. Although she was badly frightened Jade's eyes took in at a glance the beautiful lamps, exotic leaves spilling from urns and expensive ornaments in Laurent's house. There were plump sofas and chairs, upholstered in blue and white linen, and they encircled a low round and outsize coffee table. The huge carpet was Persian and the ceiling was beamed and tall candles stood in beautiful candle-holders, no doubt ready for any emergency, apart from the fact that they would be used for dining lighting.

'So.' He turned. 'We made it. Don't look so frightened.' His eyes went first to Marcelle and then to Jade. 'The waiters,' he said, 'had begun sticking adhesive tape across all the windows to hold flying glass when I came on the scene. Nicole was there, looking for you. She felt responsible for you and wished to take you back to her house. Then I went to Curepipe.'

'Oh.' Jade's voice was small. So that was it! Nicole had suddenly become conscience-stricken and had asked Laurent to pick her up, after they had found out that she had gone to Marlow's plantation-house, and after Laurent had made certain that Marcelle was safe. Obviously he had intended that Marcelle would take shelter in his home.

Marcelle was saying, 'But, Laurent, why talk now? I can't stop shivering. My hair—I wish to dry it. Although I had my raincoat, my blouse is still damp.'

While Laurent helped Marcelle off with the rain-coat Jade could not help noticing that the blouse in question had a sexy, lingerie look and that the material was soft and silky and sensual. 'You know where to go,' he was saying. 'You'll find towels,' he touched Marcelle's hair with his fingers. 'Okay?'

When Marcelle had left the room he asked, 'How wet are you?'

'Wet enough.' She shivered. 'I have jeans and a shirt in my case. I was going to work at Marlow's house, you see. I noticed that—that ...' somehow she could not bring herself to say Marcelle, 'Miss Fabré did not carry a case, and I was prepared—and so I also have a spare sun-frock and a caftan. She can choose what she wants.'

Ignoring her offer, he snapped, 'What were you do-ing there? Demonstrating that you are practically Mrs Marlow Lewis?'

'Yes,' she said, feeling inflamed because Marcelle Fabré obviously meant so much to him that he had gone to Curepipe to check on her safety, immediately warning of the cyclone had been given. 'Marlow phoned me from Reunion just before I left, as a matter of fact. We'll be married soon.'

'How soon?' His strange green eyes raked her face.

'At the moment I can't say. I know it must have been a nuisance to you when Nicole suggested it, but thank you for bringing me here. I was terrified at Marlow's house.'

'Well, you will have to get used to Marlow's house, no? After all, it has been standing long enough. What made you go there, when you saw that the weather was changing? Sometimes you seem incapable of serious thought!'

'I wasn't to know there was going to be a cyclone,

was I? It had been a beautiful dawn.'

Something crashed somewhere and she caught her breath, and put her hands to her face. 'This is hideous! I don't know how you kept the car on the road.'

'For that matter, neither do I,' he answered. 'I can't say how long we are going to be trapped here, but we might as well resign ourselves to the fact that it will be for some time. However, there is always food in this house and candles, lamps. Come.' He took her arm. 'This is what I refer to as my den,' he told her. 'It used to be a double garage, but I had another garage added which leads directly into this, as you saw for yourself ... a precaution against bad weather. I do not have to leave the car in order to get into my house.'

Marcelle Fabré was in the lounge when they got there. She was crying quietly as she rubbed her dark hair with a towel. Looking at Laurent through the towel she said, 'I cannot even telephone my mother. The phone is not working, Laurent.'

'That is something which cannot be helped. It goes like that. Try not to worry.' His voice was almost gentle and Jade watched as he placed an arm about the other girl's slim shoulders.

'It is not easy,' Marcelle answered. 'I have no clothes ... nothing.' Her eyes went to Jade's small case.

'I haven't much,' said Jade, 'but what I have, I'm willing to share with you.' She was thinking that Laurent's cool, composed business manager was really going to pieces—not that she could blame her. They could hear the roar of the wind and the rain as it lashed the roof, shuttered windows and walls. 'What it must be like at Marlow's house, which is built of tropical wood, I shudder to think.' She glanced at Laurent.

'It has stood the test of time,' he replied shortly. 'Come,' he said to Marcelle, 'I will give you something for your nerves and maybe you will be able to relax on top of your bed.'

It seemed obvious by the way in which he had spoken that Marcelle was a frequent visitor to his house.

Laurent came back into the room. 'You will have my room,' he said. 'If you are ready, I will show you where to go.'

'But surely....' she began, but he cut her short.

'But nothing. We could be here for as long as four days.' There was always this sense of ruthlessness about him, she thought resentfully, which made him difficult to argue with.

'I'm ready.' She gave him a level look.

He seemed to prefer off-white, she found herself thinking, but this was possibly to show off to advantage his possessions, which were obviously rare and certainly very beautiful. The thick carpet was off-white and so were the low sofa and chairs at one end of the room, which had brilliant scatter cushions in shades of sunset colours and green. Windows and doors were shuttered, to protect the glass from the howling wind and torrential rain which was sweeping the island.

Jade caught her breath when he placed his arms about her and felt her clothes for dampness. 'You'd better change,' he said. 'Come through to the lounge when you are ready and we will have something to drink, and then, seeing that my Creole couple have gone to take shelter in their own home, you will help me to prepare something to eat. Marcelle is too upset.'

She inclined her head. 'Fine.' Tensely she watched him as his eyes went to her mouth, then he trailed his fingers lightly beneath her chin and then down to the hollow of her throat. 'Dry your hair. By the way, you will find my bed most comfortable.'

The radio was on when she got back to the lounge and, while Laurent poured drinks, they listened to the weather reports. Warning four stated that cyclone conditions existed over the island.

'How is Marcelle?' she asked, in a stiff little voice.

'Marcelle is worried and upset.' His voice was abrupt.

'W-what about dry clothing? I've offered her what I have,' she said.

'It is quite all right.' His voice was cool. 'She has changed into one of my silk shirts. It is too hot for much else. She also has a splitting headache. By the time we left my shop there was no time to contact her mother. We went straight to Marlow Lewis's house.'

'It's a pity Nicole involved you—with me, I mean,' she ventured, 'although I'm selfish enough to be grateful. I—I hated it at Marlow's ... all this wind and rain ... and of course, it's got worse.'

'I was able to find out from Philipee where you were,' he said.

'On the way to Marlow's,' she said, 'there was this wind, which I'd noticed before. Broken branches were flying about in the dust—not big branches, but bits and pieces. It felt like something was wrong.'

'And yet you remained at the house, instead of going back with Philipee?' He passed her a drink and their fingers touched and, as usual, Jade felt the shock of excitement.

Turning away from him, she felt an emptiness that surely must be as bad as Marcelle's splitting headache due to the fact that Laurent had snubbed her invitation to lend Marcelle a change of clothing.

Moodily her eyes travelled around the room. More plump sofas, covered in a woven off-white fabric and French silk sofa pillows, appearing almost gem-like in the light from the lamps. An exotic cane sofa-table stood behind one of the sofas where there were stre-litzia flowers arranged in a vase. A fat candle stood on an elaborate brass candlestick. An Oriental lamp cast a glow in the room. There were side tables accommo-dating costly things.

'You are looking at all the candles, maybe?' He sounded amused. 'For obvious reasons, I keep my house stocked with them. At any moment the power could be cut.'

Jade's eyes went back to the outsize coffee table which held English brass antique candlesticks.

'Your home is very beautiful,' she said. 'Your indoor plantings are very lush.'

'Normally they get the light from the French doors, which are all shuttered now, as you can see.'

Often there was noise of something smashing, some-where, or the sound of something heavy being blown away. 'When will it ever *stop*?' Jade cried, her nerves on snapping point.

'It has only just started,' he told her. 'Make up your mind to this. It is for the people who really know poverty that I feel sorry. Tin shanties are blown away. Even in the better built homes, doors are smashed in and windows sucked in and shattered. Roofs are torn off. Everything seems to go mad for a while. But it does not happen very often, so cheer up.' He gave her a smile. 'But while it does, crops are pressed into the ground, there are wash-aways and between the wind and torrential rain and high seas we take a smashing, despite precautions.'

At that moment Marcelle came through to the room wearing a white silk shirt which showed her long slim legs off to good advantage. 'I am desperately in pain, Laurent.' She began to pace about, pushing long, slim fingers through her dark hair.

He got up and guided her down to the sofa, beside him, and then cradled her head against his chest. 'You must relax,' he told her.

'I can't! My mother....' Marcelle began weeping again.

'Your mother would have shut herself in by now. God knows there are enough warnings over the radio.'

'What can I do to help you, Marcelle?' Jade asked. 'Let me massage your scalp for you.'

'There is nothing you can do.' Laurent sounded irritable. 'Marcelle is plagued by migraine headaches. In a moment the pills will begin to help. They always do.'

With gathering resentment Jade watched his fingers as they went up and into Marcelle's silky hair and then suddenly he stood up and gathered her into his arms. 'You must lie down,' he said. 'I will make a wet cloth for your eyes.'

When he came back he poured fresh drinks for himself and Jade. 'What are you thinking about?' he almost snapped.

'I keep thinking about Marlow's house,' she lied.

'Marcelle thinks of her mother. You think of Marlow's house. Anything else?' He put her glass down beside her. 'Marlow's—lovemaking, maybe?'

'I was thinking of his cane-fields. You mentioned crops, a moment ago, being pressed into the ground.' She did not try to hide the fact that she was angry.

'Well, you have reason to think, my dear girl.

Cyclone Carol, for instance, cut the 1960 sugar output and almost put a halt to the tea industry, I believe. I myself was here in 1970 when Cyclone Hermine caused much damage. *This* cyclone might well bring the famous hunter back—for that very reason.'

Taking a sip of her drink, Jade said, 'What you are trying to convey, of course, is that the threat to his cane-fields might cut short his business visit to Re-union, whereas my arrival here didn't bring about this turn of events. Is that it?'

'Yes, as a matter of fact that is exactly what I am try-ing to convey. This must be upsetting for you.' He sounded anything but sympathetic.

'It is upsetting,' she answered hotly, 'for the simple reason that Marlow....' she broke off as something heavy crashed outside and then they were quiet for a moment, as they listened to the fierce squalls of wind and rain ... an awesome sound.

'Anyway,' Laurent went on, 'these tropical revolving storms pass close enough to the island to bring about cyclonic winds and torrential rain on only four days a year, so you need not be unduly worried. Cyclones severe enough to cause great devastation have only occurred twelve days in ninety years.'

'It doesn't seem like it now,' she commented, still feeling ruffled with him and on edge because of what was taking place on the lovely island.

'Considering the risks,' his green eyes met hers, 'you still intend to remain in Mauritius?'

'Of course. I have no option,' she replied, without thinking.

'What do you mean you have no option?' He went on looking at her.

'Well, I've come here to work at the health hydro

and, later, to be married, after which I intend to continue with my work. As a matter of fact, Marlow is in complete agreement.'

'You will work until you have Marlow's baby, is that it?' He turned that dark sea-green gaze on her again.

While something within her shrieked ... Oh no, don't *say* that! I don't want a baby by Marlow, she said, 'Possibly. I don't know.' She lowered her lashes and began swirling the liquid around in her glass.

'What is in this drink?' she asked, after a moment, to break the silence between them.

'Rum and fruit juices,' he told her.

'It's delicious. I always imagined rum to be a sailor's drink.'

Suddenly he set his glass on the side table next to the sofa on which he was sitting. 'I must go and see about Marcelle. One moment, please.'

Jade, sipping her rum and fruit juices, watched him. Well, she asked herself, what had she expected? That Laurent should sit and make flighty talk over the wind and rain and smashing and tearing noises, while Marcelle tried to cope with her migraine and the worry about her mother?

She was walking about the room, drink in hand, when he came back into the room. Without turning she said, 'I'm admiring the beautiful assemblage of objects and furnishings. I hope you don't mind?' She knew that her voice had only succeeded in sounding tight, instead of careless, which was which she had intended it should be.

Immediately she had come into this room, her eyes had searched for the white jade phoenix which he had described to her, but when she had spotted it she had been determined not to remark on it.

'Marcelle is far from well,' he said. 'She is very upset over this whole thing.'

'Well,' Jade could not stop herself from saying, 'I guess she isn't the only one on this island who happens to be very upset right now. Perhaps, on top of every-thing, she's upset that I'm here?'

'Don't be sarcastic with me,' he snapped. 'I am not in the mood for it. Take my advice, make the best of things here.'

'Oh, but I am.' She spoke lightly, but her blue eyes were furious. 'I've changed, as you can see.' She turned round and her amber-gold silk caftan swirled out-wards. 'I'm having a drink; I'm admiring your beauti-ful collection. I was hoping that Marcelle would make use of this caftan,' she shrugged. 'However....'

Suddenly he caught her wrist and impelled her to look at him. 'In other words, you are bothered by the fact that she is wearing one of my silk shirts?'

'Not at all,' she replied. 'What would you like me to say—*yes*, I *am* bothered?'

Suddenly the lights flickered and went down and, just when they thought they were going out, they brightened. They stood listening to the water noises and the force of the wind, which seemed to shake the house to its foundations.

Laurent released her wrist. 'Tell me,' she said mock-ingly, 'what would happen if the house came down?'

'Seeing that I have told you that mine was the sort of house a knowledgeable Mauritian would build to see himself through cyclones, I would feel very em-barrassed.' He had, she noticed, changed into dark low-belted slacks and a soft bronzey-melon coloured shirt which emphasised his exciting dark skin. His eyes went over her. 'You wear this caftan with a romantic air.

Let me get you another drink ... and then we will see about this meal.'

While he passed her the glass he said, 'So you like my house?'

'Very much.' She still did not know how to take him.

'I am one of those fortunate people whose professional occupation coincides with their private tastes. I like to live with these things.' He sat down on the opposite sofa. 'In a way, I regard myself as a custodian.'

'Your shop in Curepipe must surely enjoy an international reputation,' she said.

'It does,' he replied, and at that moment the room was plunged into darkness and the lights did not come on again. 'One moment.'

Apparently they both moved together—Jade from fright—and then, still holding her glass, she found herself in his arms and the warmth of his body against her own was like an electric shock. Because she felt she ought to, she tried to draw away from him, but her heel caught in the hem of her caftan and to prevent herself from falling, her free hand went to his arm.

'Don't fight me,' he said.

'M-my glass,' she murmured. 'Be careful, Laurent, your carpet....'

In the darkness she felt him take the glass from her fingers and knew that he was groping for a place to set it down.

When his arms tightened about her and his lips came down on her own she felt herself go weak all over. 'Don't muddle my life,' she whispered.

'That shouldn't be hard, because let us face this, you don't love Marlow Lewis.'

Against all the dictates of common sense she allowed him to cup her small breasts with his hand, for she realised that to him she was just one of many. And then his fingers were in her hair and, as her lips parted for him, she made no effort to control the excitement he aroused in her, that almost suffocated her. He strained her thighs tight against him and something in the tenseness in his lean body made her realise that he was experiencing the same sensation. Her heart was thumping so hard that she was afraid he could feel it through his silk shirt.

When she managed to free herself she said, 'You frighten me so much when you kiss and hold me like this.'

'Why is that?' He reached for her in the darkness again.

'Because, right now, I want it so much. Tomorrow I'll hate myself.'

'In Mauritius we have a saying,' he said, 'and that saying is—tomorrow belongs to no one.'

'Laur-rent?' It was Marcelle. 'The lights have failed now. Oh, I cannot see a thing with all the shutters fastened! Come and get me, *please*...!'

Swearing softly, Laurent released Jade. 'I am searching for matches,' he said. 'There are candles all over the place, but I have mislaid the damn matches.'

Jade stood perfectly still, hating him, hating herself and hating Marcelle Fabré for the shock her voice had caused to her clamouring nerves.

Laurent lit one candle and then another, and soon the beautiful room was glowing with flickering light. The French silk sofa pillows in sunset shades appeared jewel-like on the off-white sofas.

'I'm terrified,' Marcelle whispered. 'Although I was born on the island I cannot get used to the weather we have at times.... This, of course, is the real thing, not just a storm. I must take my sleeping pills. I must escape from all this!'

'Don't be nervous.' Laurent went over to her. 'It will take a lot to flatten this house, and try not to worry about your mother. Your brothers were on their way to your mother's house, after all. If we managed to get here in time, they will have got there in time.'

'We shouldn't have come here,' Marcelle went on, her voice rising. 'If you had not gone to Marlow Lewis's house we should be at *my* house, right this minute. I'll never forgive you for what you have done!' Suddenly she began to sob hysterically.

'Tell me where your kitchen is,' said Jade, wanting desperately to escape from this scene. 'I'll—if you give me a candle, I'll go and see what I can do so far as preparing a meal is concerned....' She flinched as the tempo of the wind increased, and bit her lip.

'Stay where you are,' Laurent snapped. 'Let me get this girl settled and then we'll see about food. Sit down!' He stared at Jade, who stared back at him. She knew her voice would tremble if she spoke back to him, so she kept quiet.

She sat on the sofa and Laurent was gone for some time, then he came back into the room. 'She is asleep,' he said.

Jade's look was hurt and enquiring, as she looked up at him. 'We'll go to the kitchen now,' was all he said.

His kitchen was in earth-tones and bore the stamp of efficiency. Many of the utensils were copper and glinted in the candlelight. Opposite the wall-fitments and usual accessories there were floor-to-ceiling windows, but these were completely shuttered. Whoever looked after Laurent Sevigny's house in his absence had been to work at the first radio warning that the island was directly in the path of a cyclone. Laurent lit a kerosene lamp. It was nothing short of nerve-racking in the kitchen which seemed to be taking a smashing on the window side, and Jade knew without being told that had those windows not been tightly shuttered, and if any of the wind from outside had got into the house, the entire glass wall would have been sucked out—or blown in, she was not sure which. The thought caused her to tremble as they prepared salads and cheeses.

'What about Marcelle?' she asked, when they had made the coffee on a spirit stove.

'There is nothing for it but to let her sleep,' he replied. 'She was insistent that she take a sleeping pill. I supervised this—in case she took more than the prescribed dose. She can eat when she wakes up.'

They carried everything through to the dining-room with its round oak table and Windsor-back chairs.

Hanging from the beamed ceiling a heavy iron chandelier mocked them, reminding them that there were cyclonic conditions and a power cut.

Laurent opened wine and glanced at Jade. 'I probably have too many plants and flowers and too many candlesticks in my home, but I like them, and that is why they are around.'

'To me it's all perfect.' She spoke in the carefully modulated voice she always used when she had been hurt and felt unsure of herself. 'It's all very English. It makes me feel just a little homesick, actually.' Her eyes went to the eighteenth-century pine Welsh dresser and English Derby plates and part of an impressive cache of copper. Then, because she had been hurt by his attitude, she said, 'We sit here and talk about too many this and too many that—plants and flowers and candlesticks, when all the time I know and you know that

bringing me here was merely the act of a damned fool.'
She expelled an angry breath and looked down at her
plate and tried to fight the tears which threatened to
come.

'Well,' his voice was hard, 'aren't all men fools, when
it comes to women?

'Marcelle resents my being here,' she said.

'Marcelle manages my shop, not my life,' he answered curtly.

Outside, the wind carried the sound of something
being snapped in two.

'It must be quite late,' said Jade. 'How much more of
this?'

'It is after ten,' he told her, and they drank their
coffee in silence and once, when their eyes met and
held, she dropped her lashes—and with them her
hopes that she would ever get over Laurent Sevigny.

'Would you like to go to bed?' he asked.

'I'll rest on top of the bed, after I've done these
dishes. It would be impossible to sleep in these conditions. In the end you begin to feel your nerves are
snapping. Apart from the cyclone, I'm hating this now.'

'I am not exactly enjoying the situation myself,' he
answered. 'I didn't exactly intend this—the three of us
in this house. You could call it a mistake.' There was a
small quirk at the corner of his mouth.

'What you mean is that you meant to drop one girl
off first. Is that it?'

'Yes,' he replied, with a deliberate, brutal carelessness.

A wildness came over her. 'Which one?' She con-
demned him with her blue eyes.

'I have learned one thing: you never tell a woman
too much. I'm too much of an expert to answer such a

question.' His eyes brushed over her.

'There's that girl in there,' she went on, unable to stop herself, 'and there's Nicole de Spéville, a woman much older than yourself, but very beautiful, and that's all that counts with you....'

'Let me make a suggestion,' he said, 'keep Nicole out of this. You are treading on thin ice, I am warning you.' There was, she thought, looking at him, something about him which indicated that he was capable of a steely violence. In fact, in his dark, low-belted slacks and soft silk shirt, the colour of an over-ripe melon, he must surely resemble the handsome, dashing corsair types who had lived by plundering the high seas.

'I find you insulting,' he said. 'So do me a favour and keep quiet.'

Wide-eyed and thoroughly aroused, she retorted, 'I won't keep quiet! You had no right to bring me here. I was the one who was insulted. I offered Marcelle something to wear and she ignored my offer and you went one better ... you refused outright. You'd rather have her walking about half-naked in one of your silk shirts than wear a caftan of mine. *I* am the one who's been insulted. This house must be to you like—a lair was to the French swashbuckling corsairs ... a spring-board for your affairs.'

Suddenly he stood up and came round the table to her side and, grasping her by the shoulders, forced her to stand up next to him, so close that their bodies were touching. 'Don't attack me with barbed remarks,' he snapped, those strange dark, sea-green eyes blazing down at her. 'You make me want to lose my temper.'

'I'm not afraid of your temper,' she stared back at him, 'and that must bother you quite a lot!'

'Let us put it this way,' he told her. 'I am afraid of my own temper, and for this reason I will react by curbing it ... this way.' She watched him, as he bent his head to kiss her. He kissed her sensually and slowly and she did not struggle, except to keep her lips cool and unresponsive beneath his own. His arms tightened about her and she felt the shivering waters of desire for him. It was an effort to bring up her lashes and she allowed them to rest on her cheeks. Suddenly her mind took precedence over the demands of her body and she struggled free.

'You are a dangerous character,' she told him, her voice shaking. 'A man of experience. A man, once he gets going, who has the know-how to take a girl out of her depth, before she quite realises what it is that's happening to her.'

'And you don't consider Marlow Lewis a man of experience?' His voice was hard and mocking.

'Marlow happens to be my future husband. I accept him for what he is.'

'Because you are in love with him?' His eyes mocked her.

'Yes.'

'So? You are in love with him.' It was a statement, but the tone of his voice was disbelieving. 'There have been times when I have found this hard to believe.'

'I regret being involved with you,' she said. 'For—allowing you to—touch me.' She almost spat the words at him.

'So you have felt yourself—involved?'

'You know perfectly well what I mean. You made sure that I was involved with you. To a point, I admit you were successful, but let's just put that down to the fact that I was feeling let down, because Marlow was away, and—*bored*.' She bit her lip, longing to take the words back.

When he spoke, his voice was cold. 'Well, it isn't the end of the world for me. Maybe I was bored too. No?'

CHAPTER SEVEN

THE cyclone, despite radio warnings and despite precautions, left a trail of damage. Buildings were wrecked, tin shanties had been lifted up and blown away, crops were flattened and there were wash-aways. The cyclone had ripped through the island and Jade knew enough, from Marlow's letters, to realise that the island did not have to be hit by a cyclone to cause havoc. Even on the fringes, hundreds of kilometres from the rotating eye, there could be high seas, fierce winds and torrential rain, as the ripple effects were felt.

It had lasted three days. Laurent Sevigny's house, which had been safely shuttered against the cyclone, was opened up. The hurricane shutters which had been clamped over the huge, view-framing windows to protect them from exploding were gradually being opened. One broken pane during a cyclone, Laurent had said, was enough to let in a rush of wind strong enough to lift a roof.

There was a pink sunset.

Marcelle's nerves had gone to pieces, and moodily Jade had watched Laurent pacify her. At the present moment Marcelle was sleeping off one of her tranquillisers and Laurent was saying, 'Come with me to the patio. We have to face up to the destruction sooner or later.'

'I feel completely stunned,' she said, when they were standing on the patio. 'It's terrible. It's so sad.'

Only the coral reef in the distance was still beautiful and, of course, those fantastically-shaped mountains to one side of the house.

The garden was a mess. Ornamental urns had been heaved over and some had been broken. So had a statue of a girl.

'Is the girl Virginie?' Jade asked.

Turning to look at her, he said, 'So you know about Virginie? Virginie flatly refused to disrobe in the presence of the slave who braved the turbulent surf to rescue her when the *St Géran* foundered Overcome by grief, Paul fled into the forest where he died of a broken heart. Eventually, Virginie's body was recovered from the sea and the two lovers were buried together. It is fiction, of course, concerning these two characters, but it is surprising how many Mauritians believe this novel to be true. The sad fate of the one hundred and ninety-two passengers of the *St Géran* inspired French novelist Bernardin de Saint-Pierre to adopt the *St Géran* as a background for his famous novel *Paul et Virginie*.'

When he had finished speaking Jade sighed as she gazed about her.

'The flower beds are reduced to nothing,' Laurent said, beside her. 'Look at that flight of garden stairs, the brain-child of my architect, left high and dry....' Jade was surprised when he took her hand in his. The desire to comfort him was almost overpowering.

'It's such a shame,' was all she could say. 'I'm sorry.'

Trees had been uprooted and so had several beautiful coconut palms.

'Everything is calm now, of course,' Laurent's voice

was almost bitter. 'The cyclone is played out. Look at the sky ... that beautiful pink. In the hotels, white-jacketed barmen will be trying to act as if nothing has happened while guests will be wondering whether in fact anything has happened, or whether it has just been a bad nightmare.' She heard his small unsettled breath. 'I have grown to understand these changes of moods on the part of the island. To cope. But many cannot cope. Like my poor Marcelle in there.' Jade felt herself stiffen. 'Her head is going to be a damn sight worse when the side-effects of all the pills she has swallowed begin to hit her.' With his free hand he patted the hand in his and, dully, she looked down. Even though she was tanned, her hand in his was much lighter. 'You, of course, took everything in your stride. Good for you!'

The pool, which was usually the colour of a sapphire in the sun, was filled with thick brown water.

'Only the coral treasures of the reef will have been unaffected ... safe in their underwater beds,' Laurent said, releasing her hand.

Suddenly, Jade thought, pacey Sydney with its touches of Victorian–Manchester-like architecture seemed very far away ... so did London.

'The roads will be potholed and practically washed away,' said Laurent, breaking into her thoughts, 'but somehow, in the morning, I must get Marcelle home. You will remain here until I get back.'

'W-why must I remain here?' she asked, confused.

'Because you are in the other direction.' There was a degree of annoyance in his voice. 'It will be impossible, under the circumstances, to do the two trips at one time. Don't you see?'

'Yes, I suppose so.' She felt the sting of tears, possibly

because she was tired and had been under considerable strain, regardless of the fact that he had remarked that she had taken the cyclone in her stride. As she stared at some broken stone steps and smashed pink geraniums she bit her lip as they blurred.

'You are to stay here. Until I get back tomorrow,' he said again.

'You make me feel like a prisoner,' she said, in a small tight voice.

'You *are* a prisoner.' The tone of his voice was marked by mockery. 'The roads will be washed away, the lines down and you cannot escape. Like my beautiful jade phoenix.'

'The phoenix rose from the ashes,' she said, 'didn't it?'

'Yes, that is so. It rose from the ashes to live through another cycle. Note, I said another cycle—not cyclone.' He laughed a little and placed an arm about her shoulder. 'However,' his voice changed, 'if you will remain on the island, it is on the cards that you will live through another cyclone.'

'There's no "if" about my remaining here on the island.' She moved away from him.

'Come,' he said, 'the sky is now a chalky-grey. Let's see whether Marcelle has decided to wake up.'

Marcelle joined them for the meal which they had by candlelight. She was still wearing the silk shirt which Laurent had given her, over her slacks. Her ivory face was paler than usual, and there were dark rings beneath her eyes. 'I feel awful,' she said. 'I can't eat.'

'You must eat,' Laurent told her. 'You cannot live only on pills.'

'Don't turn on me, Laurent.'

'I am not turning on you. I am trying to help you. In

the morning I will take you home.'

'And Miss Lawford?' Marcelle's eyes raked his face. 'What about her? You will take her home at the same time, maybe?'

'It will be impossible to do the two trips. The roads will be in ruins, if my garden is any indication of the havoc caused by the cyclone. You are worried about your mother and for this reason you will go home first.'

'You sound irritable,' Marcelle said. 'It is not my fault. I did not expect us both to be here.'

'No.' His voice was dry. 'That is so, Marcelle. Neither did I.' After a moment he said, 'We might all be cut off here, for all I know. I can only find out in the morning.'

Jade closed her eyes in frustration. 'I wish I could make a plan to get away, believe me. I don't know how to go about it, though.'

'It is a pity Laurent brought you here,' Marcelle's voice rose. 'What is the pudding there? I might have some of that.'

'It is mango mousse,' said Laurent's Creole house-keeper, coming into the room. 'I am not yet organised in the kitchen. I made it with tinned cream. It whipped, I thought, quite well.'

'No,' said Marcelle. 'Not with tinned cream.'

They drank coffee in the lounge with its off-white sofas and French silk sofa pillows in those exciting sunset shades, as Jade thought of them. Beautiful lamps awaited the return of electricity to light them, but at the moment, there were candles which flickered on top of large brass candlesticks.

When Marcelle began to sob quietly Laurent said, 'You are worn out. Let me help you to bed, Marcelle.'

He was gone a long time, it seemed to Jade, and

then, when he returned, she said, 'You appear to have involved yourself in a situation which is an impossible one. I'm madly embarrassed, believe me.'

'I did not arrange the cyclone,' he said.

'You know I didn't mean that,' she said hotly.

'What do you mean, then?'

'I'm woman enough to know that Marcelle Fabré is jealous because I'm here. It's not for me to—reassure her.'

'Don't worry,' his voice was hard and careless, 'I have—reassured her. But let us put this on record, Marcelle is a girl who is as beautiful as a cat, and very often she behaves like one. However,' he flashed her one of his corsair smiles, 'I have admiration for both. Into the bargain, Marcelle also happens to be a very capable business woman. I admire this trait also, believe me.' The candlelight exploded tiny gold flecks, which she had not realised were there, in the sea-green eyes. 'She receives a very good remuneration for managing my business.'

Jade stood up and left the table to stand at one of the French doors. The sea sounded very loud. She stood with shoulders drawn up high. Everything was so unreal. She tried to visualise the hotel and the health clinic, but couldn't. The cyclone seemed to have washed everything else from her mind, except that she was in love with Laurent Sevigny and was bitterly jealous of Marcelle Fabré ... the girl who was as beautiful as a cat and, very often, behaved like one. Laurent had admiration for both the cat and her spiteful tantrums.

Behind her, Laurent, dark, lean and strangely green-eyed, looked devilish in denim pants and a white silk shirt, which was open half-way down. Even standing here like this, without seeing him, she was aware of him ... wanting him, as she had wanted no man before in her life. She stood very still, looking out at the blackness which was the coral reef. There was the eerie white line where the breakers plunged down on the reef.

'What are you thinking?' he asked, from behind her.

Encouraged by the wine they had drunk with their meal she said, 'If you must know—you.'

'What about me?' He put an arm around her waist.

'When you make love to a girl, is your approach direct, even savage? Or is there a gentleness, hidden there under that hard, hard surface? There, does that satisfy you? It must do. You're the type, after all, who goes to art galleries in France, when you're there ... opening nights in London, when you're *there* ... and to bed with any beautiful girl who happens to take your fancy.'

'And this worries you, of course?' He laughed softly and touched the nape of her neck with his fingers. A little shiver ran through her.

Suddenly he swung her round to look at him and her caftan made a silken swish. She tried not to let her eyes go to where his shirt was unbuttoned and where his flesh was tanned and hard ... and a little on the hairy side, but only excitingly so, to remind her of his strength.

For several moments they studied each other and then, tentatively, their lips met and he drew her close. Jade could feel the beating of his heart against the flimsy material of her caftan. She knew that she felt tired beyond belief and yet excited beyond belief.

'Don't try to mask your desire,' Laurent murmured against her mouth. He caressed her breast with his finger tips and she allowed him to get away with it. 'You seemed to have missed the whole point,' he went on, 'as to why I brought you here.'

Drawing away from him slightly, she said, 'I know why you brought me here, don't worry. It was just a pity that it backfired for you. You couldn't get me back in time and you were landed with me.' Her resentment burned while her senses screamed with longing for him. For several moments she stood staring at him and then he drew her close again. The desire she felt for him began to climb—like flames, leaping in a grate, she thought a little wildly, as she clung to him.

'Persistently, you always bring up the subject of other women,' Laurent said, holding her away from him. 'Why don't you forget them? Maybe they don't exist?' He laughed softly and brushed his fingers beneath her chin.

'I suppose you think that sounds like—half-way—into getting me into bed with you, when your house-keeper has locked up for the night and gone to her husband in the cottage you provide for them?'

'You are way ahead of me,' he said. 'I was not thinking along those lines ... not with Marcelle in the house.'

'And we seem to be stuck with Marcelle tonight, don't we?' Jade felt furious with herself for inviting his ridicule and, no doubt, contempt.

'A new element has crept into your way of thinking,' he said, very softly. 'Am I right? With Marcelle out of the way....'

'Let go of me!' she snapped and, as she left the room, she thought she could hear him laughing at her.

After breakfast which she ate alone on the ruined patio she went into the broken and smashed garden.

timidly at first, because she was still nervous that the
weather might suddenly change, and then gaining confidence because everything seemed so calm. Then she
made her way to the beach where she stood, huge sunglasses blotting out her blue eyes, and gazed at the
sea lagoon and coral reef beyond. Laurent and Marcelle
had already left and she felt alone and frightened-as
she thought of a possible tidal wave. It was difficult to
believe, however, that after all the hell which had been
let loose, there was this calm.

Several coconut palms lay across the beach and there
was a lot of driftwood about—and seaweed and even
shells. She turned to look back at Laurent's house,
which was on a promontory over the ebb and flow of
the sea lagoon and coral reef. Steps led down to an
empty stretch of sand and, in calm weather, it was obviously an ideal blend of house and sea—but it also
opened to the impact of that Indian Ocean and its
violent moods.

The design of the house was amplified by its rough
trowel-stucco finish. To achieve integration of design
with sea breezes and ocean, glass walls could be pushed
back to admit those breezes and the sounds of the surf
on the reef. Fortunately, all of those glass walls and
windows could also be shuttered against them. With its
views and expansiveness, the house had drama ... like
its dark owner, Jade thought. It was a house where, indoors, art wove an intensely personal theme, with the
sea beyond remaining the dominant presence. Even its
very handsome owner could not dominate that presence, she thought.

Later she went back to the house and walked about
admiring Laurent's beautiful possessions. Many of the
possessions, she noticed, were of jade—China's most

precious stone. Jade, like the idiotic little name her mother had insisted upon. Gleaming, luminous jade. Laurent Sevigny obviously experienced an appreciation of it, she thought, and felt a little shock of excitement at the idea. There was the jade phoenix, with its long, splendid tail feathers and crested head.

By late afternoon she began to grow restless. A double captive, one of Marlow Lewis and the other of Laurent Sevigny.

She was still wearing her denim pants and a shirt when Laurent arrived back, and one look at him told her that he had had to push his car out of mud and slush.

'So . . .' she felt confused and at a loss with him, 'you managed to get through?'

'Yes, but it has taken most of the day to do it, as you can see. Still, I got her home and that is the main thing. The island is badly hit, I'm afraid.'

'And her mother?' Jade felt compelled to ask.

'Fine. Hysterical, of course . . . like her daughter. She didn't know where Marcelle was.' His strange green eyes went over her. 'How have you been?'

'Okay. I was beginning to worry, though.'

'And now?'

'Well . . .' she shrugged, 'I'm glad you're back, naturally. I didn't fancy being here alone tonight. I mean, I don't know what turn this calm weather might decide to take.'

'It is unfortunate for you that there is no electricity and therefore no hot water. Are you "into" cold showers?' Suddenly he smiled at her.

'I—I don't mind,' she shrugged. 'I've enjoyed them.'

'Okay, then I leave you. I myself must shower and change. Later, we will walk down to the beach to see what is what, and then, when we get back, I'll pour you a very good drink.'

'Fine.' She inclined her head slightly and made no mention of the fact that she had already been to the beach.

After she had showered and changed into her caftan she went through to the lounge to find him already there. 'We'll take our drinks to the beach,' he said.

Jade watched him as he poured their drinks and, to make conversation, she said, 'I've already been down to the beach, as a matter of fact.'

'Oh?' He turned to look at her. 'How was it, getting down there?'

'I managed,' she shrugged her shoulders. 'Your garden steps still exist, even though they *are* suspended in mid-air. Your pool, of course, is a mess.'

'I have got off lightly, believe me.' His eyes were serious. 'By rights, I should be out there helping, but I am selfish enough to want to turn a blind eye to it all.' Their eyes met.

The sunset, when they got there, was a magnificent profusion of pinks, crimsons and apricot, and it flushed the white beach, sky and Indian Ocean. Even the palms which had been bent right over and were lying across the sand looked romantic, until you realised that they were there as a result of a devastating cyclone which had hit the small island, Jade thought. Where filaos were growing on the lawns their roots had been left exposed where the sand and the lawns had been washed away. There were no small catamarans on the sea lagoon this evening. Something had happened to this strip of paradise.

Jade slipped her sandals with the glittering stones from her feet and walked on ahead of Laurent. She carried her drink in one hand and the sandals in the other. Some of the coral which had been washed up dug into her toes. The air smelled heavily of sea and sea things. On the reef, the breakers were high and loud.

'Here,' said Laurent, beside her, 'let me carry your shoes. Or better still, put them down here.'

'Look what it's done to your beach!' There were tears in her eyes. 'Just look—palms and trees completely uprooted, things washed up.' Her voice broke.

His voice, when he answered, was curt. 'I said to forget about that now. Right now we will enjoy the calm after the cyclone. In other words, we will count down. Tell me,' he put her sandals down beside some driftwood and took a sip of his drink, 'what did you do with yourself today?'

'I came here.' She lifted one shoulder. 'I'm not sure if you'll like this. . . .'

'Try me.'

'I walked around your house, something like window-shopping, and looked at all your exciting and beautiful things.'

'So?' He sounded pleased and interested. 'You saw my jade collection, in that case?'

'Yes. I was very interested, seeing that my name is Jade.' She gave him a smile.

'I like to live with these things,' he told her. 'I like everything that makes my life agreeable but most of all I have, ever since I can remember, had a passion for jade.'

Jade began walking again. Under normal circumstances, it would have been an unforgettable experience, strolling in the sunset on the beach of an island with a man with the devilish, handsome looks of a dashing corsair—or as she and, no doubt, countless other women imagined a corsair might have looked in those far-away days.

'It was, of course, inevitable that a beautiful and difficult girl by the name of Jade should enter my life,' Laurent remarked.

'Why difficult?' she asked, turning, and hoping a little wildly that he might tell her that he was in love with her—hopelessly so, since she was here to marry another.

'Just think about it,' he told her, and something inside her hurt.

'I have,' she replied, thinking of Nicole de Spéville and Marcelle Fabré, quite apart from the others who were, as yet, nameless to her. 'To get back to my name, though,' she decided to change the subject. 'My mother must have been very romantic to have wanted to call me Jade. When time begins to create havoc with my face it's going to sound very stupid being referred to as Jade.'

Laurent put out a hand to halt her and then he touched her cheeks with his finger-tips. 'With your bones,' he said, 'there will be no havoc.'

Compulsively she moved towards him, conscious of his body, slim but hard and strong and darkly tanned —but in any case, his skin was naturally dark. Her eyes went to his mouth, chiselled and fascinating. Her expression was brooding and quiet—and very still. He drew a long breath and she heard it. His arm slipped around her waist and he drew her to him, and his eyes seemed to change colour. Those strange dark sea-green eyes could play havoc with a woman, she found herself thinking as his mouth came down on hers. While she responded to him one sentence hammered away in the back of her mind—well then, Miss Lawford, you know the set-up here, don't you?

'Let go of me,' she said, moving her head to one side. He went on kissing her cheek and she struggled against him. 'May I remind you that I've come to Mauritius to marry Marlow Lewis?'

'Have you?' His voice sounded lazy and bored and slightly mocking. 'I think it is you who needs to be reminded.'

'Is there no possibility of getting me back to my hotel?' she asked.

'No possibility. It took me most of the day to get Marcelle back home. In places, roads are completely washed away.' Suddenly, and like the corsair-type she imagined him to be, he grinned. 'You are my prisoner. Come.' He stooped to retrieve her sandals from the sand, where he had placed them earlier. 'What is bothering you?' His green eyes mocked her.

'What do you expect to be bothering me?' she asked. 'You have a mind like a computer so far as women are concerned.'

'I was hoping that this kind of conversation could have been avoided,' he said.

The beach looked gilded now. The pink, crimson and apricot was fading and everything was turning to gold, even the green fronds of the palms which had been left standing and the ones that had fallen across the beach.

'Would a computer collect beautiful things?' he asked, and his voice sounded careless.

After a moment she said, 'I wouldn't be surprised if your feelings over your collection of beautiful things are superficial.'

'That was well thought up.' He turned to look at

her. 'It must give you a glow of satisfaction, no, to have thought of it? You are really very incredibly young.'

'I suppose, compared to Nicole, I *am* very young.' She could not resist the barb.

'That is what I mean,' he said. 'Compared to Nicole, you are very young.' He gave her a strange look. 'It is as well that you begin to know the score.'

'I only passed a simple, reasonable remark,' she replied hotly, 'and that was to the effect that you let go of me.'

'Give me your glass,' he said. 'Did you enjoy your drink?'

'Yes, thank you.' She could not trust her voice.

'You even ate the pineapple—and the cherry.'

'I know,' she murmured, her lashes down.

'It is an accepted part of life, here on the island, that piece of pineapple fastened to the rim of the glass and the cherry at the bottom of it. Things can be very good here, or they can be very bad—or both. Like now.' He took her hand. 'Let us not speak without thinking.' He said this with unusual gentleness.

Jade walked back to the house barefooted and then, after brushing the sand from her feet, went inside to the lounge. While Laurent mixed fresh drinks she walked about the room, still in her bare feet.

'You've seen it, of course,' Laurent spoke, without turning. 'The *féng-huang.*'

'The—*what?*'

'The *féng-huang,*' he repeated 'or phoenix, which brings peace and prosperity to the realm.'

He came to stand beside her, and passed her the glass which was draped with pineapple.

'That is an interesting piece of jade you are looking at. From time immemorial, the Chinese have associated spiritual and moral values with jade.' Their fingers brushed as she took the glass from him, thrilling at the touch of his skin upon hers.

'I see,' she murmured. 'Well,' she took a sip of her drink, 'although my name happens to be Jade, I know nothing about it, I'm afraid.'

'The ancient text of the Li Chi has it that knowledge lies in the luminous quality of jade, eternity in its durability, purity of soul in its rarity and, of course, its spotlessness; moral leadership in the fact that it goes from hand to hand without being tarnished, benevolence in the gleaming surface and uprightness in its unyieldingness.' His eyes held hers.

'The one cancels the other out,' she said.

'So? In what way?'

'On the one hand it goes from hand to hand, without being tarnished,' she said, 'and on the other it's described as unyielding. What about power? Haven't they come up with something about power?'

'As a matter of fact, yes, they have. Power lies in its harmlessness. I have the power, of course, you the unyieldingness.'

'I had no idea that so much importance was paid to jade,' she said.

'The word is appreciation,' he told her. 'The appreciation of jade is enhanced by intimate association. This applies to the real thing and not just the girl Jade.' His fascinating mouth mocked her. 'In the case of the two forms of jade, nephrite and jadeite, association with as many examples as possible leads to this appreciation. Each piece holds its own identification. There can be, however, only one girl Jade. Although I already feel I know her well, my experience with her has not been what can be described as an intimate association.'

'It's been intimate enough, for all that,' she answered shortly, 'considering the—circumstances.'

'If you have intention of referring to Marlow Lewis, I am possessed by the absolute determination that we are not going to talk about him.' The cool voice and hard green stare were back. 'For one thing, I do not have much time for Marlow Lewis.'

'So I gathered,' she said, and began walking about the room again, drink in hand, touching this and touching that.

'While we are together, in this house, we will not talk about him. We will talk about us.' He lifted his glass in mocking salute. 'When I am alone with a girl I do not want to drag in a third party.' Those dark, sea-green eyes held hers with a look that was as disturbing as the touch of his fingers, the feel of his lips on hers.

'In this case, the third party happens to be the man I'm going to marry.'

'Yes.' His eyes looked scornful as they went over her. 'But you overdo it. Why not just leave it until he gets back.' It was not a question, the way he put it. It was a command, merely formed as a question. 'In that way you can see what is what.'

'I know what's what!'

'Don't get ahead of yourself!' Suddenly he expelled an angry breath. 'I am not given to excess, or dramatic, statements,' he told her. 'I am merely suggesting that you forget about Marlow Lewis. When he gets back you can begin to take stock.'

'But stock of what?' Jade swung round, her blue eyes furious.

'You might have to be prepared for a change.'

'In Marlow? Or myself?' She shook back her dark hair.

He shrugged and turned away.

'You think I might have made a mistake?' she asked, willing him to tell her that this was what he did believe and that he was in love with her. At this moment she was more than ready to confide in Laurent Sevigny and to admit that she was in love with him and had, in fact, never been in love with Marlow.

'Are you afraid of making mistakes?' he asked.

'Well, of course.' Moodily, she watched him as he picked up a silvered crane on a malachite base and then put it down again. 'Aren't you?'

Looking at her, he said, 'Perhaps one of the most fortunate things that ever happened to a man is that he doesn't have to pay as much for his mistakes as a woman. Women are very like the treasures you see here, in my house. They are here to be enjoyed ... often casually.'

'I realised that those are your views, soon after I met you,' she said. 'That's what I'm afraid of. There have been moments with you when I feel ... well, I see myself as your victim.'

'In other words, you want me to make love to you. You want this as much as I want it.'

Her heart froze at the words. You want me to *make love* to you. Not—I love you.

'Are you. ...' she broke off and then went on again, 'Are you suggesting that I allow you to make love to me, tonight? Now that Marcelle has gone?'

She was quick to notice the click of surprise in his eyes. Almost in one step, he came over to where she was standing. His face was very close to her own and she froze with the completely unexpected fury she had apparently just unleashed in him. 'I have never been willing to settle for second best. There is enough in life that is second best. I don't have to settle for that.'

Because she was nervous, Jade took a sip of her drink and stared back at him, resting the rim of the fragile glass against her lower lip, after she had done this. In her billowing caftan, the background of the beautiful room they were in was melodramatic and appropriate. His skin, which was like copper, was perfect for the clothes he was wearing—dark slacks and a white silk shirt, open at the chest. His dark hair was elegantly long in the neck.

'Is that what *you* want?' he asked, his green eyes going over her. 'Second best?'

'No. That's just it—I don't want second best,' she replied, taking the glass from her lips.

'No? Well, it is something you might well have to learn to cope with.' His voice was dry. 'But not with me. When I take you you will be yielding, with none of the unyieldingness of jade. There will be that luminous quality of jade about you, however, and I don't have to supply you with a reason as to why it will be there ... but while it is there, there will be no ifs and buts floating about in your mind. But forget about this now. Forget, also, about wash-aways and cyclones and the destruction caused by them.' He took her glass from her. 'One more drink before dinner. No ...' he held up a hand, 'they are really very light.'

She had been shocked by his temper, she found herself thinking as she stood there helplessly, watching him as he poured drinks. He was the most devastatingly handsome man she had ever seen in her life. Everything about him was exaggerated in her mind. His eyes were so strange, darkly green one moment, and yet, with the tawny lights in them, much lighter the next. His mouth was perfectly moulded, but there was nothing soft about it. Jade had seen it looking more than just a little hard from time to time. He was completely male and, despite his leanness, gave the impression of great physical strength.

Without turning, he said, 'Don't look at me like that, Jade. And do not be nervous of me. I have been ready to quarrel with you, but let's forget that now.'

'No,' she said, 'we should have had a quarrel before now. Now we both know how we stand.'

'We do?' Turning, he laughed softly. 'So? We know how we stand?'

'Yes. At any rate, I've come to my senses,' she told him.

'About Marlow Lewis?'

'Yes, about Marlow. And about you.'

'What about Marlow?'

Her long dark hair slipped forward as she looked down at her bare feet. 'Well, I realise that I—love him.'

'And me?'

'I've come to my senses about you. What do you want me to say?' Her eyes were troubled rather than angry.

'You must answer for yourself. However, there is no need to give me an answer. Women are natural liars, anyway.' He laughed softly, but his eyes were cool. 'Here is your drink.'

'You mix drinks with cool expertise,' she said, taking it from him. 'I thought island cocktails were potent? I shouldn't be having this.'

'This caution of yours!' He sounded frankly irritable. 'It is a pity you did not put it into practice before coming here to marry a man you hardly know and one so much older than yourself.'

'As usual you go to extremes,' she answered.

After dinner, which really was very good, considering, Laurent said, 'I have a very good tape recorder, operated by batteries—for an emergency such as this. I think we could do with some mood music. We will go, I think, to my den.'

When they were there Jade remarked, 'It's hard to believe that this beautiful beamed room, with its attractive bar, used to be a garage. I love your plump blue and white sofas and chairs. The Persian carpet, of course, is perfect for them.'

'As you can see,' he said, 'I also collect blue and white ginger jars and antique plates.'

'And plants,' she smiled, and bit her lip.

'I am very French and from France,' he said, 'and in many ways this looks like a room might very well look in France. I wanted this room crowded with everything I like.' He began looking out tapes. 'At night, lit by candlelight, it is a kind of paradise on a paradise island. I have too many plants and too many flowers, when I happen to be here and when my garden has not been flattened by a cyclone, and I have too many candlesticks and too many blue and white ginger jars. I know all this, but I don't care.'

Jade found herself laughing easily with him. 'I think the whole house is beautiful,' she said.

'I enjoy a dialogue between all these objects,' he went on. 'It's a place of poetry and,' he shrugged his shoulders, 'privilege, if you like, for I feel privileged to own so many beautiful things. Nevertheless, they are here to be enjoyed and looked after—not worshipped, by any means. Good, here are new batteries. Let there be no mistake, while I enjoy candlelight from time to time, I also enjoy the benefits brought to us by electricity.'

Jade walked about the room, which they had not used while Marcelle had been there, admiring everything. 'How beautiful,' she said. 'Bronze leopards inlaid with gold, isn't it?'

'My own appreciation of them is high,' he told her.

When the music started she felt her nerves tighten, for the tune he had chosen was *The Way We Were*, which someone had whistled as the plane had lost height and prepared to land in Mauritius. It was also a tune which she had grown to identify with the island, for she had heard it constantly since her arrival. She was surprised when Laurent said, 'It seems a long time since somebody whistled this on the plane.'

When the excitement she had felt on hearing this particular tune had died away she almost hated Laurent Sevigny for awakening the feelings she had been trying to tame.

The candlelight did dramatic things to her blue eyes and they widened a little as he walked towards her. For several moments, in the flickering light, they studied each other and then, tentatively, their lips met, very gently at first and then finally with abandon as his arms closed about her.

Her fingers went to his dark hair which was springy where it grew down to his neck. His body, lean and hard against her, made her feel as if she was drowning. Behind the lids with their extravagantly long lashes her blue eyes were blind with fright as she realised the longing he had aroused in her.

'Don't,' she whispered. 'Unlike you, I can't accept the male point of view about my physical needs.'

'Don't push me too far,' he snapped. 'You do not

know what you want. Forget the games and let's get down to self-honesty.' He held her away from him and looked into her eyes.

'Second best doesn't seem to worry you, after all,' she said, on a hard little breath. 'You—you've *got* to believe me! I don't know how I've allowed myself to drift into this, but I'm—enormously in love with Marlow. I'd never forgive myself if. . . .'

'That is a strong statement. You want to get yourself together.' There was hostility in his voice. 'However, I find you more than just a little useless and I have no intention of haggling with you. Haggling is an act of trade. One haggles in Port Louis when one wishes to buy something and therefore it is not undignified. But I do not want to buy *you* with fancy phrases and fancy set-ups.'

Jade watched him while he switched off the tape-recorder and as he left the room. She was shaking and her eyes were suddenly wet. A rare carving of malachite, the colour his eyes had turned as he had released her, Shi Shi lions, playing with the sacred jewel, wavered before her.

In the morning he took her back to the hotel. The road was a nightmare of wash-aways and this alone prevented conversation, but something told her that even if they had been on a magnificent motorway, Laurent Sevigny would have had nothing to say to her.

CHAPTER EIGHT

MANY of the poorer people, living in tin shanties, had been left homeless and were still in packed cyclone refugee centres.

The hotel gardens, too, had suffered and many of the palms had been left standing but were stripped away, on one side. Others had been toppled. Filao trees had been uprooted or stripped of all foliage.

Several times on the journey, Jade had thought that Laurent would have to turn back because, in places, there just seemed to be no road upon which to travel. However, searching for a way out, he seemed intent on getting her back to the hotel.

Finally, when they had reached the hotel, he turned to look at her. 'You know where to find me,' he said.

'Thank you—for rescuing me,' she said, confused and upset. 'I would have been terrified otherwise.'

'For sure.' His voice was polite, nothing more.

As she got her key from reception she tried to ignore the feeling of emptiness in her. Staff members were still busy in a kind of mop-up operation but, strangely enough, apart from the stripped gardens and temporarily ruined pool everything seemed fairly normal.

There was, unbelievably, hot water and she suspected that the hotel must have its own emergency generator. After a shower, she changed into slacks and a halter-top and went to the health clinic. Here, amid louvred doors, exotic plants and lotions, the conversation was mostly 'Cyclone Fraziska'. Most of the Creole staff were absent—cut off from the hotel. There was no sign of Nicole de Spéville.

One of the clients was saying in a pettish voice, 'I was led to understand that most cyclones pass Mauritius by. I wouldn't have come, otherwise.'

'Mauritius lies in the south Indian Ocean cyclone belt, mod-dom,' the Creole beautician answered, 'but it is true, most cyclones do pass Mauritius by. You can't judge us by this one.'

Nicole came to the clinic the following day, wearing one of her caftans, and apart from shadows beneath her eyes, she looked beautiful. 'When did you get back?' she asked Jade.

'Late yesterday afternoon,' Jade replied. 'It was a marvel we got back, actually.'

'I looked everywhere for you,' Nicole went on. 'I was going to take you to my house at the first warning, and then I heard that you had gone to Marlow's house.' Her voice sounded flat.

'I decided to spend the weekend there,' Jade told her. 'I thought I'd find something to do there—you know, like washing curtains.' She felt suddenly foolish.

'Laurent arrived,' Nicole said. 'He was rushing up to Curepipe and when I told him where you were, for I had found out by that time, he said he would contact you.'

'How did you cope during the cyclone?' Jade asked.

'Oh,' Nicole shrugged, 'I was alone. We all got cut off somehow. My brother stayed here.' Her voice sounded almost accusing now. Obviously, Jade thought, Laurent had put Marcelle and his business before Nicole.

For days the island was busy mopping up and repairing the trail of damage caused by Cyclone Fraziska. There were many sunken boats to salvage. The famous Garden of Pamplemousses, lying beneath the

Moka Mountains and which had been created in 1767, had been greatly damaged. Beautiful mountain rose trees had been stripped or blown down, it was reported. Spice plants and bushes, cinnamon, cloves, nutmeg, pepper and ginger had been flattened. Ornamental trees, palms, creepers and shrubs had either been greatly damaged or completely destroyed. Fraziska had torn her way through this place of peace and calm, flattening and tearing up crotons, teak trees, raffia palms, camphor trees, shanties, buildings, crops and whatever lay in her path.

In the health clinic, louvred doors swung open and swung closed again. Water noises came from rooms with cool tiled walls and floors. Things were back to normal and Jade went back to her salon in the vaulted arcade.

Surrounded by flattened cane fields, Plaisance International Airport, which means the Place of Pleasure, was open once more and Mauritius, the island of pungent spices, white beaches, violet, mist-veiled mountains and forests, had once again become a busy crossroads of the ocean. Regular arrivals and departures of jets flying in—and out—from Africa, Europe, Asia, Australia and neighbouring islands of Reunion, Madagascar and the Seychelles were in operation once more.

Marlow Lewis flew in from the neighbouring island, Reunion.

Jade was in her room when he knocked. She had bathed and was dressed for dinner and when she opened the door she caught her breath.

'Hello,' he said. 'Remember me?'

'W-when did you get back?' she stammered. 'Come in.' She stood to one side, to allow him to pass into the small corridor, with the bathroom to one side and walk-in wardrobe to the other. Closing the door, she said, 'Where would you like to sit—in my room, or the balcony?'

He remained standing and then, placing both hands upon her shoulders, he kissed her very lightly on the mouth. 'I'd forgotten how young you are,' he said.

Because she felt it was expected of her she said, 'Not so young, really.'

There was, she found herself thinking, a faintly chilling quality about Marlow, which she had not noticed in Australia—but then she hadn't been engaged to him then. Was it this deadpan coolness about him which accounted for the fact that he was well known, here on the island, as a hunter? His hair was still the reddish-blond colour she remembered, like his beard and moustache, and although he was in his forties, he seemed to have an instinct for contemporary fashion and was very 'with it'.

The hardness about Marlow was for real and it was difficult to believe that she and Jeffrey had lived with him in Australia and that he had been broken enough by Elisa's death to give up farming and to leave Australia for Mauritius. What was even more strange was that he had, after a period of corresponding with her, asked her to join him on the island and to marry him.

Still standing, he said, 'I am sorry I couldn't be here when you arrived.'

'Oh,' she shrugged and tried to smile, 'I know it couldn't be helped.'

'I'm back earlier than I intended,' he went on. 'I wanted to see how my place fared after the cyclone.'

So he had been worried about his sugar estate. His concern had nothing to do with her.

'And how did it fare?' she asked, although she had

actually been there at the beginning of the cyclone.

He let out a long breath. 'Flat. Cane fields flattened —the lot. Some of my outbuildings were wiped out.'

'And the dogs?' she asked.

'How did you know about the dogs?' His voice was sharp.

'I-I was there—at the beginning,' she stammered, not reminding him of the fact that Laurent Sevigny had taken her there before that.

'Oh yes, I know about that, but from what I was able to gather you were not there long enough to find out about the dogs.'

'How did you know I was there?' Her eyes widened.

'Nicole told me.'

'Oh, I—see.' But she didn't. 'I—I didn't know.'

She watched him as he sat down on a peacock chair.

'I didn't know you hunted,' she said, taking the other matching chair opposite him. A small round cane table divided them.

After a moment Marlow said, 'There's a lot you don't know about me, let's face it. Am I right?' He smiled faintly.

The thought depressed her and she said, 'Well, yes, I suppose so.'

'From my house you went with Laurent Sevigny to his house,' Marlow went on. 'I'm still trying to work that one out.'

'There was another girl there,' Jade said quickly. 'Her name is Marcelle Fabré and she manages his business in Curepipe.' She laughed lightly. 'Everybody in Mauritius says Kuur-peep or something.'

'I know her slightly,' he said, 'but go on.'

'At first I thought she was his girl-friend—but I'm not sure.'

'Why aren't you sure?'

'Well, there's Nicole de Spéville,' she replied, and suddenly Marlow laughed. There was some amusement on his face, but this amusement did not reach his eyes, somehow.

'Are you jealous?' he asked.

'No, of course not. Why should I be?'

'I'm asking *you*.' His light brown eyes went over her.

It was all very strange, Jade thought afterwards. After asking her whether she had enough money, Marlow had left her. His kiss had been anything but demanding. She sat for some time thinking about him. He had been wearing denim pants and a denim jacket, like a man half his age. Actually, he was the type of man who would have the power to make other men of his own age appear older. And yet he had made her feel very young and unsure of herself. Her thoughts were chaotic. While she had dreaded any intimacy on the part of Marlow Lewis she had not bargained for the pre-occupied manner in which he had handled their first meeting on the island.

Because she felt unsettled and upset she decided to go for a walk before dinner along the beach, and slipping off her gold sandals she hooked the straps through her fingers. The crimson caftan she was wearing curled about her ankles in the light breeze which sprang off the sea. Even with the uprooted palms, the beach was beautiful in the sunset. It was the kind of exotic setting to make a girl feel beautiful—but Jade was feeling anything but beautiful. Nothing made sense to her. When she turned her head, she could see Laurent Sevigny's pink-dusted chalet.

There was white spray where the breakers pounded the reef, but there was hardly any sound. All was calm.

Sea, sand and sunset, she thought, gazing at the ocean.

Back at the hotel the barman would be busily polishing glasses and the wine stewards would be handing out snacks to go with sundown drinks. It seemed foolish for her to remain here—for she knew without a doubt that she could not marry Marlow. In fact, he himself appeared stunned that he had landed himself in the position of having sent for her.

A curving, empty beach, she thought, a little wildly, and an empty, utterly drained girl—for suddenly she felt just that. Drained. Her crimson caftan blew against her thighs as she stood lost in thought, gazing at the sea lagoon and the vast Indian Ocean beyond the reef.

'I would feel a lot easier if you knew I was here,' Laurent Sevigny said and, wide-eyed, Jade swung around. 'I have been standing here for some moments, just watching you,' he went on, 'and waiting for you to come back to earth.' He smiled and lifted one shoulder.

'I was—thinking,' she stammered. She had not seen him since the day he had dropped her off at the hotel, after Cyclone Fraziska.

'This is a moment I love,' he said, pleasantly enough. 'Sunset on the island. Often, like now, I take a walk along the beach. Not often do I come upon a beautiful girl in a crimson caftan, with the sea breezes blowing the garment against her and hinting at the exciting chic slimness of her.'

'You're exaggerating, of course,' she said, a little breathlessly, amazed that he appeared friendly. 'There are always beautiful girls on the beach here, no matter what the time. This evening happens to be an exception.'

'You look lost—and alone,' he said, coming towards her.

'It's quite simple. I *am* lost and alone.'

'But your future husband, the great hunter, is back, no?'

'How do you know?' she asked.

'The whole island knows that the great Marlow Lewis is back. I've noticed this thing about you,' he went on easily, 'your eyes are never quite the same colour.'

'It's something I've noticed about you too, as a matter of fact,' she replied, 'but in any case, it's something I can't change.'

'I was not objecting, believe me.' He laughed softly, easily, carelessly. 'Tell me, what is it you were thinking about?' he asked.

After a bitter little moment she said, 'I was thinking about the beautiful water hyacinth which may soon strangle waterways and rivers in Australia.'

'Really?' He threw back his dark head and laughed, and the laughter registered disbelief. 'So?' He sobered. 'You are interested in the beautiful water hyacinth?'

'Very.'

'So interested, in fact, that you can think of nothing else at a time when the man you are to marry has returned?'

'I've already said that I'm very interested in the water hyacinth.'

'I am, too. This must come as a surprise to you. But I am also interested. Did you know that recent studies of the sex life of this giant plant revealed that it can double its number in about ...' he shrugged, 'ten days? That means to say that two beautiful hyacinth blooms on the bank today can be, let us see, yes ... two hundred and forty thousand in ninety days.'

'Yes, I knew that,' she replied tartly. 'I've made a

great study of the sex life of this giant plant.'

He laughed again, his sea-green eyes going over her.

'So? You surprise me,' he said.

There was the sound of water slapping against the glass-bottomed boat which was used to take tourists out to the reef.

As usual, Jade found Laurent's closeness exciting.

'Don't be cautious with me,' he said. 'Just be candid and tell me that the meeting up with Marlow Lewis was a disaster.'

'Anything *but*,' she replied, in an angry voice. 'It went off very well, actually.'

'Oh, well,' he said, with a deliberate, brutal carelessness, 'it is a matter of indifference to me, anyway.'

'I must go,' she said.

'I have a perfectly good Chinese dinner waiting at my chalet,' he told her. 'It seems a pity it is going to be eaten by one person.'

'If this is an invitation. . . .' she began.

'It *is* an invitation.'

'Well, I've never eaten Chinese food. I might not like it, but thank you just the same.' Her voice was stiff.

'If you have never eaten it then you are in for a pleasant surprise. Chinese food can be excellent. You will enjoy it—fish and poultry, soups and excellent sauces, sweet and sour. Roast and diced chicken with walnuts, fish in bean sauce, crab fried with chilli and ginger, prawn cutlets. You can choose between bird's nest soup and shark's fin soup. This is Cantonese.'

'This isn't what your cook has prepared for one, surely?' Her voice was sarcastic.

'Well, no, of course not. I am giving you an example of Chinese food. I will take you to eat in Port Louis—in the Chinese quarter which never sleeps.'

'I can see myself coming.' Jade spoke with a touch of defiance and turned away, pushing the tears back up her cheeks with her fingers so that he would not see them.

'You will come,' he said casually, 'just as you will come to my chalet now.' He took her by the shoulders and turned her round to face him. 'Don't fight me. You do not want to go back to the hotel, and you know it.'

With a feeling of helplessness she said, 'All right, I'll come.'

'Good. Although there is a perfectly daunting menu waiting for you at the hotel you will be doing yourself a favour by sampling my cook's excellent Chinese dinner.'

The beach and the sea had disappeared behind the screen of darkness which had now fallen and, far out, the coral reef was just a white smudge.

In Laurent's studio, Jade stood watching him while he fixed their drinks.

'You go to a lot of trouble,' she said, 'frosting the rim of the glass and all. What is it?'

'The white of an egg and caster sugar,' he told her, adding a sprig of mint to the cherry in the drink. Then he sliced a tiny pineapple and slipped a piece on to the rim of the glass. 'You and I will always be at war,' he glanced over to her, 'but that does not stop us from drinking together, surely?' When he smiled, she noticed the groove in his cheek which somehow she had overlooked before.

They took their drinks out to the balcony. The stars were thick and one in particular looked as if it was about to plop into the blackness of the sea. Down on the lawns the lanterns were lit and there were people walking on the paving stones as they made their way to the hotel dining-room from the chalets which they occupied.

'So?' said Laurent, when they were seated on the cane chairs with their silk cushions. 'I take it you did not set the date?' It was difficult to judge, by the tone of his voice, whether he was being sarcastic, or not.

Pretending ignorance, she said, 'The date—for what?'

'For your marriage to the hunter.'

'That will follow. He was worried. After all, his cane fields had been flattened by the cyclone.'

'For sure.' He made a face and shrugged. All very casual, she thought bitterly, with the thought of getting away from this part of the island growing stronger in her mind.

After a moment she felt compelled to go on. 'It was strange, you know—I mean, I haven't seen him for quite some time. He—he seemed so cut out for Australia—I—can't describe it.' She placed a thumbnail against her teeth. 'Australia seems to be made for Marlow. Well, he is Australian, after all. I understood him there—the farmer, the sheep station. . . .'

'He is still a farmer. He owns a sugar plantation, after all, no?'

'Yes, I know. He seemed to have forgotten how—how young I am.' Jade broke off quickly, annoyed with herself for playing into Laurent Sevigny's hands. 'But it's the privilege of the bride to have butterflies, after all.'

'For sure,' he said again. He sounded almost uninterested.

Something drove her on. 'I can't marry Marlow,' she said. 'I—don't love him. I was a fool to come here.'

'Now that you have actually confirmed what I already understood,' he said, 'I just can't believe it. You don't love him?' There was astonishment in his voice. 'You have gone out of your way to prove to me that you did.'

To hide her humiliation she said, 'I'm in love with someone else ... in Australia. As soon as I can get some money together, I'm going back, with my pride in my pocket.'

'You seem like a girl who goes through life taking chances,' he said, and he spoke with such indifference that Jade despised herself for having confided in him in the first place. He turned his glass round and round in his fingers and then he looked up. 'And you, of course, still have to tell Marlow Lewis all this?'

'Yes.' Her mind raced ahead. 'He looked so tired that I didn't tell him.'

'Oh, I don't know.' Laurent lifted his shoulders. 'Perhaps he was merely looking his age?'

Abruptly he stood up and went into the studio, where he poured himself another drink. When he came back to the balcony again Jade said, 'I don't want to talk about it any more. I'm sorry I started all this. We never talk about *you*—it's always about me.'

'By that you mean that we never talk about my love life? Is that it?' His eyes met hers.

Suddenly she could stand it no longer. 'Yes,' she said. 'I'm very much aware that it exists.'

'So you are aware of this?' He regarded her face with something like amusement. 'I don't mind telling you a bit about myself. My father made me a partnership to an extensive range of investments, directorships and chairs on various boards. I travel a lot, but I have made Mauritius my base. Above all this I have, as you already know, my own personal business here on the island.'

'Which Marcelle runs for you.'

He ignored the remark and went on easily, 'Did I tell you about my beautiful sister?'

Hurt, because he apparently could not remember what he had told her and what he hadn't, Jade said, 'No, you didn't.'

'Well, she is very classy, very cool and elegant and she has a smart address. She is married to a successful man.'

'The successful Sevignys,' she said, in a hard little voice.

'So you are going back to Australia—to this man?' His eyes went over her.

'Yes.'

'And in the meantime?'

'In the meantime I'm going to enjoy the island sun, palm-fringed beaches, turquoise sea. I'm going to eat fruit at breakfast time and drink daiquiri cocktails in the evening before dinner, and later, I'll dance to one of your twing-twang Sega bands. While I'm doing all this, I'll be earning money to go back. However, I'll be moving to another part of the island. I don't want to go on staying here.'

'Already you sound happier.' He came for her glass and she felt a hopeless fury build up inside her that he seemed oblivious to the fact that she was at breaking point. 'You are a girl who takes chances and one who gets over things quickly. However, you could do all those things on this part of the island. Why move?' He sounded merely polite.

He brought her another cocktail and as he passed it to her he said, 'Well, here's happiness. Here's to your Australian ... your other Australian.' His eyes mocked her.

'And here's to your—er—lady-love, whoever she happens to be. I can never work that one out,' she said.

'Oh,' he shrugged carelessly, 'you wouldn't be interested.' His voice sounded lazy and bored and slightly mocking. 'As a matter of fact, I thrive on variety. You know,' he looked down at his glass, 'I have been thinking.' He lifted his lashes and met her eyes.

'What about?' There was interest in her voice now.

'I have been thinking that before you go back we should have a romance.'

After a moment she said, 'Are you suggesting that I should—fall in love with you?'

'I was not suggesting that. However, it would certainly help the romance along. Many island romances go on here and then,' he lifted a shoulder, 'when they are over, that is that. She goes back to her life—he goes back to his. It is as simple as that.'

'This is, in other words, thriving on variety?' Her blue eyes were angry.

'Yes.'

'And this is really what you wanted, before Marlow got back, isn't it? You wanted an island romance, as you call it.'

'For sure. The idea gave me great pleasure ... especially as you yourself appeared eager for it. Actually, you might welcome such a romance when things begin to wind up here for you.'

'Yes, I might.' The island, the coral reef and island cocktails were beginning to work on her and she felt suddenly reckless. 'Yes, I might at that.'

'It is on the cards that you will,' he said.

'All right.' Her face was pale now. 'When do we start, Mr Sevigny? *The* successful Mr Sevigny, that is.'

'Tonight ... now, but I am warning you, you could

be asking for trouble. If we embark upon this island romance I must prepare you for the fact that I will go out of my way to make a casual romance look like the real thing.'

After a moment she said, 'Well, fine—and that must make you dizzy with success, mustn't it?'

She watched him as he came towards her and then, taking her fingers in his own, he drew her up beside him. Then he took her glass from her and put it down on a nearby table. Don't let me cry, she was thinking; don't let me cry. . . .

'Are you afraid?' he asked, before he took her into his arms.

'No.'

'I was serious,' he told her. 'I want to go as far with you as I can.'

'You could say I've just become a "good-time girl,"' she said, in a hard little voice. 'You show me the island, the Chinese cooking, the Creole and French cooking, market places and pink sunsets and then I'll go back . . . with my memories. *I'll* give you—variety, the kind you thrive on,' she added with measured harshness.

He looked at her with an expression that unnerved her, then he kissed her and the kiss lasted a long time, then he released her suddenly so that she stumbled.

'Don't feel guilty over Marlow Lewis. I don't think you should even speculate about him. He himself is not absolutely gallant.'

Afterwards, Jade realised that she had hardly known what she was eating. They walked back to the hotel, along the beach and with the blackness of the sea beyond. Laurent had kissed her with passion and she had responded with abandon, while one part of her wept.

At her door she said, 'I'm not going to invite you

in.' Tensely, she watched him. 'I don't want to—to—be rushed—you know?'

Suave and handsome, he said, 'You are divided between indecision and the temptation to go on with this?'

'I *have* decided. We said we'd start at the beginning, not at the end.' She shivered, although the air was warm and scented and the corridor in which they were standing was open on one side to the sea breezes.

'In that case—until tomorrow, and the next day—and the next. Goodnight, Jade.'

She had not yet begun to prepare for bed when there was a knock on her door and, believing it to be Laurent, she hesitated and then opened it. Marlow stood there.

'I thought you'd gone home,' she said. 'Where have you been?'

'I've just come from Nicole's. May I come in? I have something to say to you.'

'You mean about....' She had been about to say Laurent, but he interrupted.

'I mean about myself and Nicole.' His eyes went over her face. 'You must have been filled in by now, surely?'

'Filled in?' Jade looked back at him stupidly, and then the reality hit her. Nicole de Spéville and Marlow Lewis. Of course! She could see it all now. Nicole's coldness, Laurent's double-talk, Marcelle's look of blank surprise.

Marlow remained standing, refusing to take one of the beautiful peacock cane chairs, but Jade sat on the side of her kingsize bed, for suddenly her legs were too weak to support her.

'Look,' Marlow was saying, 'you're a nice little kid, but that's all there is to it. At first your letters saved

me from going mad out here. Elisa was the only woman
I ever loved, believe it or not. If she hadn't been killed,
along with Jeffrey, I'd still have been sheep farming in
Australia—let's face it. I doubt it we would ever have
married. We were both drifters, but we fitted. When I
came here I had one affair after the other.'

'Even after you wrote suggesting I come here to
marry you?' Her voice was strangled, even though relief was flooding her.

'Even after that. And make no mistake, it will go on,
of that I have no doubt. I'm just made that way. Anyway, Nicole and I had something going. She'd lost her
husband. We satisfied one another's needs. She didn't
even mind when I told her about you, and then when
a vacancy for a beautician fell vacant she agreed to you
making application. But then I knew that, apart from
the odd flutter on my part, I'd reached the stage when
I wanted to let my hair down with a woman nearer my
own age. I'm—er—putting my cards on the table, Jade,
and I trust you'll keep this under your hat, but Nicole
has money. What *I* need right now to make a go of
sugar farming is money. Tonight, Nicole insisted that I
come back here and tell you that we want to get married.'

'Does she know that money also comes into this?'
Jade asked, and her eyes showed the contempt she was
now feeling for Marlow.

'Come off it. In any case, I guess I'm in love with
her. Money will help things along, that's all.'

Jade sat staring up at him. She had been going to tell
him of her relief at his news, but in view of what he had
just told her about his affairs on the island and possible
future affairs and his concern with Nicole's money, she
kept this to herself.

'It's a pity,' she said, 'that you hadn't broken the news before I left Australia, isn't it?'

'What will you do?' he asked. She watched him as he began to pace about the room. He looked rugged and strong with his almost auburn hair and beard. It was not difficult to imagine him having his way with women—and hunting down animals. At this moment she despised him.

'I'll stay on here for a while.' She got up and went to stand in front of the big glass sliding doors to her balcony. Then she slid them wide open and the sea breezes drifted in and the curtains began to float upwards and her room felt suddenly clean again. 'That's the only stipulation I have to make. That I stay on here for three months. I should have enough money by then to get me back to either Australia or England.'

'Perhaps Nicole will allow you to work on at the clinic,' he said. 'I'll talk to her.'

'It's funny,' she gave him a level look, 'but I always thought that Laurent Sevigny and Nicole were having an affair.'

Suddenly Marlow laughed shortly. 'She's years older than he is!'

'Age doesn't seem to make much difference these days,' she persisted, watching him.

'No ... I can tell you, here and now, there's nothing going on there and never has been. Nicole asked him to bring her to a couple of parties at my place, that's all. She didn't want to give rise to gossip so soon after her husband had died. A lot of people knew about us, but she tried to keep it quiet, naturally.'

'What about Marcelle Fabré?'

'I wouldn't touch her with a seven-foot pole,' he snapped.

'I wasn't referring to you—I mean Laurent Sevigny.' Her eyes never left his face.

'Oh, *him*. No doubt he's got something going with her.' Marlow spoke with a brutal indifference. 'I don't give a damn, one way or the other.'

After Marlow had gone Jade went to sit outside on the balcony. The filaos sighed and the palm fronds rattled against a background noise of the surf on the reef. Lights from the hotel made glittering patterns on the black water of the pool.

CHAPTER NINE

IN the morning she went back to a world of shadowed hibiscus-pink, apricot and gold silk and cotton curtains, honey-gold tiled floors and arches everywhere. Louvred doors swung open and shut, rustling the exotic leaves of the plants which grew in huge honey-gold urns. The health clinic was filled with subterranean sounds and slapping noises. On the other hand, Jade's salon was a rose-tinted, mirrored sanctuary, where the reception area was decorated with ancient Chinese, Japanese and Indian furniture and carved temple good-luck chairs, adorned with hibiscus-red Persian silk cushions and which Nicole had purchased from Laurent Sevigny. The chairs bore the carvings of the ancient Chinese designs on them—lotus, temple dragon and phoenix. What was it they said about the phoenix? The only bird of its kind, which after living for centuries in Arabian desert, burnt itself on a funeral pile—to rise again from the ashes to live through another cycle.

Well, thought Jade, like the phoenix she was about to burn herself. But would she arise with renewed youth? She very much doubted it. She would take back to Australia, or England, her memories and her broken heart.

While she dreaded coming face to face with Nicole she felt a wave of relief, nevertheless, when Nicole rang through for her. 'I'd like to see you in my office, please.'

Nicole was surrounded by files and brochures and people kept knocking and, in turn, were dealt with or merely waved away.

'Please,' she said to Jade, 'sit down. I will get straight to the point, I think.'

Determined to keep her feelings to herself, Jade said, 'Please do.'

'By now,' Nicole went on, staring down at her desk, 'you will be acquainted with the fact that the man you have come here to marry has let you down. No?' She glanced up and the false eyelashes she always wore made her eyes appear very big. 'For that is what it amounts to.'

'Yes,' Jade replied, 'that's what it amounts to.'

'And,' Nicole went on, 'what is more, *I* am that "other woman". I have been most unhappy. I wanted for Marlow to write and tell you this, but he could not bring himself to do it. I had thought of writing to you myself, but ...' she broke off and shrugged, 'I—I couldn't. I am sorry.'

'I sensed something, of course,' Jade replied.

'You did?' Nicole's eyes widened. 'About us?'

'I sensed *something*, Nicole. Let's just leave it at that.'

'I see. I'll be honest with you, Jade. When I saw that

you appeared interested in Laurent Sevigny I kept on hoping that you would discover for yourself that Marlow is too old for you.'

'Making a comparison didn't enter my mind.' Jade decided to keep up the tournament.

'Of course.' Nicole's voice was stiff now. 'Marlow tells me that you wish to stay on here for three months before you go back to Australia. That is right, no?'

'Yes. It's a stipulation I've made. I wish to remain on the island for three months—for reasons of my own. It will be a kind of working holiday. If I don't work here, it will be somewhere else.'

'No, no. You will work here, of course.' There was relief in Nicole's voice, but not much joy. 'That I owe you, at least.'

'You owe me nothing, Nicole.'

'*I* feel I do and, for this reason, I wish for you to take the three weeks' vacation which would have been due to you had you married Marlow and kept on working for me. No, no, no....' Nicole lifted a hand. 'I insist, absolutely. This with my blessing. *Please*. Then when matters have died down a little you will come back—until you are ready to leave. You have made a stipulation. Allow me to make mine. Beginning from tomorrow.'

Jade heard her own small, unsettled intake of breath. 'All right. If that's what you want, Nicole.'

The funeral pile will be high, she was thinking, as I burn myself. Every day for three weeks ... with Laurent. Every night....

'I wish you well,' Nicole was saying. 'You will get over this, believe me. Marlow is much too old for you, my dear.'

And for you, Jade felt like saying. He's much too old

for you too, Nicole de Spéville. Marlow is old and jaded, so far as women are concerned. Although you're his age you're obviously comparatively untouched by men—and their ways. You go to your funeral pile, Nicole, I'll go to mine. . . .

'You look so strange,' Nicole said. 'Are you feeling all right?'

'Yes. Yes, of course. I wish *you* well, Nicole. I really do.'

Laurent phoned soon after Jade got back to the salon. 'I want you to lunch with me,' he said.

'I can't see you today,' she told him. 'Nicole has insisted that I go on three weeks' leave, from tomorrow. I have things to do today.'

'This evening, in that case. I will take you to a Chinese restaurant in Port Louis, for Port Louis you have not yet seen. At night it is shrouded in mystery.'

'All right,' she said softly, and took her first plunge beneath the high cold breaker which was going to wash her up on the shore where the funeral pile was already waiting. 'By the way, I know everything. The lovers have confessed.'

'That is to the good,' he said, 'but don't tell me any more. I don't want to know any more. I feel I know it all. Until this evening, then.'

As she slipped into the soft lacy cashmere vest-dress which she had bought at the boutique that afternoon, Jade found herself wondering how many women had gone with Laurent into Port Louis at night—Port Louis which was shrouded in mystery.

'That bodice,' Laurent said when he saw her, 'and straps on your shoulders, accentuate the slimness of you—and the goldness, for you have turned very gold from the sun.'

'Thank you. For your information it's a camisole bodice and shoestring straps.' She kept her voice light.

'Into the bargain, the belt you are wearing....'

'A tooled gold leather belt and the shoes,' she stretched out a foot, 'sling-back....' Laughing a little she said, 'Okay? But in any case, I happen to be reserved about flattery. There's no need to flatter me during the island romance we're about to set into motion.'

'But the romance makes more sense to you now, surely?' His eyes met hers.

'In what way?' She waited.

'What is sauce for the goose is sauce for the gander. Our island romance will convey this message to a good number of curious islanders. It will go to show that the affair between Nicole de Spéville and Marlow Lewis has left you quite unmoved.'

'And that's why you suggested this island romance? You knew this was coming to me?' She tried to keep the bitterness out of her voice and her eyes.

'A romance, even a casual island holiday romance, is something to be enjoyed,' he said, 'not examined. Let us face facts, we both had motives when we decided to set out on it. Right?'

'Oh, yes,' she replied, deliberately sarcastic. 'Well, shall we go?'

Driving on the island at night was quite an experience.

'It's so dark,' said Jade, turning to look at him. 'Isn't it? The island, although small, seems so vast and lonely and the distance to your Port Louis long.'

'Are you nervous?' he asked, taking her hand. 'Of this darkness?'

'A little,' she laughed shyly.

They passed through one or two haphazard settlements, but the lights were not bright. The roads were still very bad in places. Some were still washed away, apparently, but Laurent appeared to know where others could be found to link up.

As they drove into Port Louis he said, 'In parts, it is very much like Chinatown, with its restaurants and gambling dens.'

'You make me feel nervous,' she said.

'One has to know where to go here.'

'And you know where to go?' She turned to look at him, loving him.

'Yes, of course. This is the seaport of Mauritius, but I suppose you know that.' Still holding her hand, he lifted it to his lips and kissed her fingers.

'I don't know much about Mauritius—only what Marlow wrote to me in his letters.'

'I do not wish to be reminded of Marlow Lewis,' he snapped.

'No more do I,' Jade replied.

The Chinese quarter glowed with light, but in places the cobbled alleyways appeared almost frightening.

'Port Louis certainly seems to be over-populated, if this is how it looks at night,' she commented.

'We are about to turn into Royal Street,' Laurent told her, 'which is the heart of Chinatown. During the day laundry flutters side by side with shop-signs.'

'Where are we going to eat?' she asked. She studied his profile in the half light and, as usual, she was physically aware of him. When she thought of leaving Mauritius she knew a moment of despair so absolute that it made her catch her breath.

'The restaurant is in a part of Port Louis which still seethes with activity when most of Port Louis is asleep.

You are not worried, are you?' As he parked the car he gave her a quick, amused glance.

'No. You seem to know all about it.'

'Do you wish to visit a casino afterwards?' he asked.

'To gamble? Do you mean to—gamble?'

He laughed. 'Only if you wish it.'

'I don't know how to. What do they play?' Looking at him, she thought he was the type of man who would create instant excitement, so far as women were concerned, at the gambling tables, with his dark good looks and sexy, darkly green eyes.

'Oh ...' he shrugged that very French shrug of his, 'roulette, dice, fan-tan, quatre-quarts, big and small ... dominoes.'

'Dominoes?' Suddenly she laughed. 'That sounds harmless enough. My grandfather used to play dominoes with me when I was a small girl.'

When they got out of the car and were standing on the pavement she said, 'It's like Hong Kong.'

'So? You have been to Hong Kong?' Placing an arm about her waist, he began to lead her in the direction of the restaurant.

'No. Only what I've seen in films.'

'I will take you to Hong Kong one day. I go there to buy, from time to time.' He spoke casually. By tomorrow he would have forgotten the remark, she was sure.

'What about opium and opium smuggling here?' she asked.

'I have no nostalgia for it.' His voice was teasing.

'I know that,' she replied, laughing a little. 'That's not what I meant.'

'Have no fear,' he said, stopping to kiss her. 'I am not taking you to a den, my darling.'

My darling. My darling.... He was not wasting any

time with this holiday romance, she thought.

They dined, Cantonese-style, on a balcony overlooking the street.

'I've never eaten shark-fin soup before,' she told him.

'Did you enjoy it?' he asked.

After a moment she said, 'I'm not sure.'

'Now what about fried pigeon, Cantonese style?' Trim and elegant, tonight—but then he was always elegant—he was wearing a dark suit.

'I don't think so. I'll keep thinking of the poor pigeon.'

'You eat chicken, though?' His eyes mocked her. Their wine arrived, and he gave his attention to it.

'All right,' she said, a moment later. 'Fried pigeon, Cantonese style, and fried prawns, with bamboo sauce.'

'Bamboo *shoots*,' he corrected.

Later he took her to the Chinese Casino, which was diagonally opposite the restaurant.

'It is fascinating, just to watch,' he told her.

Later, in the car on the way back to the hotel, she said, 'It was fascinating, but a little frightening. Everybody looked so—dedicated to gambling. And now it's so dark. The roads are so bad, after the cyclone, I don't know how you can tell where you're going.'

'I am an islander now. I know where to go. By the way, I am taking you to my chalet for a nightcap, and then I will take you home.'

'Home?' she murmured. 'Where is home?'

'Home is where you make it, no?' He turned to look at her.

'It's very late,' she told him.

'But you are on holiday, are you not?'

'Yes, but....'

He cut in, 'You are tired and crave sleep, is that it?'

His voice was sarcastic. 'How are we to have a romance if, after each time I take you out, we return to your door where I will kiss you lightly and leave, because it is late and you are tired and crave sleep?' He moved his shoulders impatiently. 'Before I get you to that door, we will go to my chalet first, where I will make mild love to you.'

'What do you call mild love?' While she was speaking her heart seemed to lurch crazily. She had never met a man with so much magnetism. He was a man who would cause instant excitement, anywhere. In fact, as she had surmised, he had created a rustle of female excitement as they had gone to stand at the gambling tables.

'Obviously you are having second thoughts,' he commented.

'No. I—I'm merely reserved as to. . . .'

'How far to go?'

'How far to go, yes—and how soon.' She swallowed. 'I've never done anything like this before.'

'That was a calculated chance I was prepared to take,' he told her.

There were shasta daisies and irises arranged in crystal vases in his chalet and Jade's eyes went to the vases almost immediately. Everything was aimed towards romance. He must have known she would come.

'The flowers are beautiful,' she said.

'Out of season, I think,' was all he said. His voice was polite. 'See the lights on the water?' He came to stand beside her. 'The fishermen.'

'Yes, I know. At night I hear them talking,' she replied. 'They shout, from boat to boat. I see their lights.'

'So you lie awake at night?' Placing an arm about

her shoulders he asked, 'What do you think of my beautiful jade?' Before she could reply he said, 'Don't tell me that you think of the hyacinth which may soon strangle the waterways and rivers in Australia. I refuse to believe that.'

Jade was aware of a current of communication between them, sharp and exciting in its message. When he took her into his arms she made no resistance and her fingers sought the angles of his cheek and jawbones, then her arms went up and around the back of his neck and she strained towards him. He lifted her hair and kissed the back of her neck, her throat. Beyond the balcony, the tide pounded the reef, and influenced by the sea they kissed more ardently.

Laurent unfastened the back of her dress and she shook her head, but he went on, his hands skilled and expert.

Drawing back, she protested, 'What about Marcelle?'

'That is a ridiculous question at a time like this!' He sounded angry.

'I've thought about this—often,' she told him.

'Well, don't think about it. Beyond any doubt, *you* are all I have in mind at this moment.'

At this moment. It was like a slap in the face and she struggled free. 'I'm not prepared to be hurried, Laurent. I *told* you.' She felt almost sick with humiliation.

'It would need a very jaded sensibility not to feel let down,' he told her, releasing her. Moodily, he watched her as she went to stand by herself, doing up her dress. He made no attempt to help her.

'I don't really feel like a drink,' she said, in a very small voice. After the excitement which she had been feeling, she felt numbed and unreal.

'I'll take you to your room,' he said, and if he was angry with her he kept the anger under control.

In the days that followed, they swam and lay in the sun on one of the white or golden beaches of the reef-ringed island. They drove out to the fantastically cut mountains. Many of the roads were still in a state of disrepair owing to Cyclone Fraziska, but Laurent seemed to find others. They ate millionaire salads—palm hearts—and poor man's 'chow-chow'. They enjoyed Mauritian cooking, a happy blend of Chinese, European and Indian recipes. From a glass-bottomed boat they admired the sea-lagoon bed, where strange 'laces', buttresses, shelves, fire coral, hard coral, soft coral, seaweeds and fish caused Jade delight.

Laurent was, she thought, the perfect companion. Slim, hard, faultlessly tanned, and exciting, he made ardent love to her, but if anything, she found herself responding to the dictates of her own straining body and certainly not to pressure from him. After the night at his chalet he seemed content not to rush her.

It was a time of moon shadows and night scents, sun and sea breezes.

Of Nicole de Spéville and Marlow Lewis they saw nothing.

The days were going far too quickly. Soon the three weeks' leave would be over and Jade would be back at the health clinic.

It was early morning and they had been swimming in Laurent's private pool. 'We are going in to Port Louis presently,' Laurent said, rolling over to look at her.

'What will we do there?' she asked. She had been sunbathing on her back and looked up at him as he bent over her. Lifting her hair from her neck he put his lips there. It seemed incredible, she found herself thinking, that this was just a game with him. Her blue eyes became serious.

'What is wrong?' he asked.

Tracing the outline of his lips, she said, 'We're always eating, Mr Sevigny.'

'You are so beautiful,' he told her. 'I. . . .'

They came apart as the young Creole lad who cleaned Laurent's chalet said, 'Miss Marcelle on the phone.'

Laurent said something in French under his breath. 'Tell her I will be there in just one moment,' he said, then Jade watched him as he went in the direction of the chalet.

While he was away she continued to lie in the sun in the pool area with its palms and tropical shrubs, cushions the colour of a newly ripened mango and sun-umbrellas. Nearby there was a blaze of purple bougain-villea. Her throat seemed to be tightening up. It was the first time that Marcelle had reminded them of her presence, unless, of course, she had phoned when they had been out.

When Laurent came back he said, 'Well, what about Port Louis?' He stood looking down at her and for a moment she felt like refusing. Instead she said, 'Fine. What did she want?' She could not bring herself to say the name Marcelle.

Shrugging carelessly, he said, 'It was strictly a busi-ness call.' Moodily, she watched him as he bent down and reached for her hand, then he pulled her up beside him.

'I'll go back to my room and change,' Jade said, be-ginning to look around for her short beach jacket. He found it for her and draped it about her slim, tanned shoulders. When he made to kiss her she stepped out of his arms. Her body was flawless and lithe. 'I'll see you later,' she said. 'I'll come back here.'

'I will drive over to reception for you,' he told her.

'What, a few metres?' Her light laugh was forced.

'Is something wrong?' he asked.

'Why ask?' She lifted a hand. 'See you!'

She wore a white slack suit with a spice-coloured scarf at her neck and a silk rose the same shade on her lapel, and on the drive to Port Louis she was quiet. Laurent's manner also seemed to have changed and he made no attempt to reach for her hand and had nothing to say.

Cars, buses and lorries filled the air with carbon monoxide. Laurent felt his way past market places, cooked-food stalls and hawkers. The streets, in places, were so narrow that Jade could almost reach out from the car and touch these things and the people concerned with them.

Chinese names hung from signboards and there was, she noticed, a bar called The Fat Cat. A heat-haze hung over the harbour, which also appeared cluttered. Laundry hung from balconies on old apartment buildings, beneath which there were shops which seemed to be beating with Chinese and Indian music. The pavements seemed to be crammed with signboards.

'It's so busy,' she said. 'It's hard to believe that this is an island. I don't know how you can bear to drive through these streets. I've never seen anything like it, honestly.'

'You will remember it well when you get back to Australia, I should imagine.' He did not look at her and gave all his attention to driving in this confusion.

'Yes.' Her voice was soft. 'I will.'

'To find parking, that is the big problem,' he went on, as he was being waved on by a traffic policeman.

'I thought you said Mauritius has a saying—it's no problem.' Suddenly she laughed, and was surprised when he flew into a temper.

'Everywhere there are no stopping signs,' he snapped. 'Can't you see that for yourself?'

There were the usual skinny island dogs, all the same shape and size, which roamed the entire island. Vehicles missed them by a mere hair-breadth.

'I usually find parking down at the harbour,' Laurent was saying. 'I think I will go back there.'

It was the first time Jade had ever seen him at a loss over something and she felt a twinge of spiteful satisfaction. There was a vitality and impatience about him, which she found endearing, as he hunted for a parking space, and the spite in her died. When he had found one he turned to her and said, 'I do not suffer fools gladly, and that policeman who waved me on just now was a fool.'

'Everybody is a fool except you,' she said.

'Exactly.' Suddenly they were laughing. 'You look radiant, cool, beautiful and very feminine,' said Laurent, 'if a little pale today. Why is this, do you think?'

'Perhaps I was jealous,' she felt reckless, 'when Marcelle phoned.'

'So?' He got out of the car and went round to her side and opened the door for her. 'Let us go and haggle for bargains. What would you like me to buy you?'

'A little phoenix,' she told him, laughing. 'Even a plastic one will do.'

They began walking. There were smells of curry, incense, hot ghee and dhal in cooking pots. Girls with rattling bangles, caste marks and marriage dots wove in and out of the traffic, which was nothing short of hideous.

'You either hate Port Louis or you love it,' Laurent said, pronouncing it 'Paw-loo-ee.' 'If you buy, be careful. Be careful, also, of so-called antiques. Many of these co-called bargains are clearly of dubious authenticity.'

'I won't be buying anything,' Jade said. 'I can't take too much back to Australia or England with me.'

What did she hope to gain by reminding him that she would be leaving Mauritius? she asked herself.

They visited shops, some of them very dark, with goods from Thailand, India, Japan, China and the Philippines. Jade examined Thai silks and cottons and Chinese shantung.

Along with other people and skinny dogs, they crossed the streets, aware of the grinding of traffic and unlike those other people and the dogs who seemed impervious to it.

Jade stepped over fermenting vegetables which had become scattered, and once when she nearly slipped and fell, Laurent caught her to him. 'Careful, my darling.'

My darling. . . . My darling. . . .

'My darling,' she repeated, laughing at him, 'isn't that cynicism?' Her hair blew across her face and she shook it back.

'Not at all. I prefer to call it irony.' The voice that had been softly caressing and agreeable had changed.

'I think I'd rather buy something from your shop in Curepipe,' she said.

'I want you to buy something in Port Louis.' His voice was still abrupt. 'Maybe you will take it out one day, and think of today.'

'What about you?' she asked. 'Will you think of to-day—when I'm gone?'

'For sure.' He shrugged offhandedly. 'I told you, didn't I, that after business hours I sit and overlook the coral reef? I have a drink and my mind seems free to think ... if I so wish.'

'Free to think of the girls you've had island romances with?'

'But this is unbelievable!' He moved away from her. 'Look in this window ... a flawless white muttonfat jade phoenix. It is waiting for you.' He put an arm about her shoulders and his lips brushed her hair and she felt like weeping at the closeness of him. 'I want you to have it. Come.'

The shop was a cut above most. They examined the eternal phoenix. Jade found herself trying to work out what it must be costing Laurent and then she said, 'I couldn't allow you to buy this for me, really.'

'Why not?' he snapped, turning to look at her in the gloomy shop. 'Tell me—why not?'

'I couldn't accept this costly thing from you.' Her voice broke suddenly. 'You—you don't have to buy me.' She put her fingers over her face.

'*Buy you?*' He took her roughly by the shoulders, while the Chinese gentleman looked on with an inscrutable expression. 'I have no intention of buying you.' Laurent's strange sea-green eyes were furious. 'Look at me!'

'No,' she said. 'I've had enough of this whole thing. I'm through.'

'Let me put it this way,' his voice was hard. 'So have I had enough of this whole thing. I love you too much for these damn silly games.'

He had forced her hands away from her face and she looked back at him through tears.

'Love me? D-did you say—*love* me?'

They had a small, excited audience now.

'Yes, I said I love you.' He shook her by the shoulders.

'But ... you said that you weren't faithful to any one particular girl—that variety was the spice of life.'

'I know I said that. What did you expect me to say —first it was Marlow Lewis, then this other man in Australia who waits for you.'

'But Marcelle?' Her blue eyes searched his.

'There has been no other woman for me—that goes for Marcelle, and Nicole as well. I knew I wanted you on that plane. What is it with you, anyway? There have been times when I have been so sure of you—sure enough to ask you to be done with this and marry me ... and then you come up with another Australian!'

Suddenly Jade was laughing and crying at the same time. 'Ask me,' she said. '*Ask* me, Laurent.'

She watched, wide-eyed, as Laurent turned to the Chinese. 'Sir, you will be my witness, no, while I ask this lady to be my wife?'

'But surely!' There was a rustle of excitement from the audience, murmurings and soft laughter.

'Darling,' Laurent's arms went around her, 'will you marry me?'

'Yes,' she answered, and bit her lip.

'And what about this Australian who waits like an idiot in Australia for you to make up your mind?'

'When I'm unhappy and jealous and uncertain,' she confessed, 'I don't create any limitations for myself. I invented him.'

'In future,' he said, 'stop to ask yourself what you're

talking about. I have a frank admiration for those who are inventors, but in this case, the inventor went too far.'

They went out into the sunshine. 'Thank you,' said Jade, 'for the phoenix, Laurent.'

Port Louis, with its teeming streets and alleyways, sagging architecture, market-places and heady scents of spices, chillies, saffron, masala, pepper and cloves, was suddenly, for her, a place of oleander and hibiscus bushes, behind old railings; a mosaic of races, customs, creeds, cultures and languages.

'Do you remember what I once said to you?' Laurent looked at her.

'You've said so many things to me ... some of them quite brutal and uncaring!'

'I said—if I touch the fingers of a girl who attracts me I have got to go as far as I can with her. There was only one such girl, and her name was Jade. Some things you don't understand. After warning one had been given I went to the hotel to look for you, and I was told that you had gone to—to this hunter's plantation house. Immediately I got into my car and rushed up to Curepipe to my business to see that all was in order there before the cyclone. I knew I had time. And then I was coming on to Marlow's house for you. What I had not taken into account was the fact that Marcelle was almost hysterical then, so I told her to get into the car and I would take her home. There is a bridge to her place and when we got there it had already been washed away. I had no option, then, but to turn back. In this area the roads are normally bad and in no time they were impossible. I got to you only in time, do you know that, my darling?' He took her fingers in his own and kissed them. Suddenly he smiled. 'And, like you said, things backfired for me and I landed up with two girls. Can't you understand—there was only one girl I wanted there? That girl was you.'

They stood crushed together in the mass of people, while he kissed her.

Harlequin Romances

The books that let you escape
into the wonderful world of romance!
Trips to exotic places...interesting
plots...meeting memorable people...
the excitement of love....These are
integral parts of Harlequin Romances –
the heartwarming novels read by
women everywhere.

Many early issues are now available.
Choose from this great selection!

Choose from this list of classic Harlequin Romance editions

What readers say about Harlequin Romances

"Harlequins take away the world's troubles and for a while you can live in a world of your own where love reigns supreme."

L.S.,* Beltsville, Maryland

"Thank you for bringing romance back to me."

J.W., Tehachapi, California

"I find Harlequins are the only stories on the market that give me a satisfying romance with sufficient depth without being maudlin."

C.S., Bangor, Maine

"Harlequins are magic carpets...away from pain and depression...away to other people and other countries one might never know otherwise."

H.R., Akron, Ohio

*Names available on request